HIGH FIDELITY SYSTEMS

A LAYMAN'S GUIDE TO THE INSTALLATION
AND CARE OF SOUND SYSTEMS IN THE HOME

SECOND EDITION

by Roy F. Allison

ACOUSTIC RESEARCH, INC., *Cambridge, Massachusetts*

DOVER PUBLICATIONS, INC., *New York*

to N. M. A.

Published in Canada by General Publishing Company, Ltd., 30 Lesmill Road, Don Mills, Toronto, Ontario.
Published in the United Kingdom by Constable and Company, Ltd., 10 Orange Street, London W. C. 2.

This Dover edition, first published in 1965, is a revised and enlarged republication of the work first published by Acoustic Research, Inc., 24 Thorndike Street, Cambridge, Massachusetts 02141, in 1962.

Standard Book Number: 486-21514-8

Library of Congress Catalog Card Number: 65-26019

Manufactured in the United States of America

Dover Publications, Inc.
180 Varick Street
New York, N. Y. 10014

TABLE OF CONTENTS

FOREWORD

WHENEVER A book such as this is written, the author is faced constantly with the task of presenting essentially technical information—information, that is, which ordinarily requires technical training to comprehend fully— in terms that are comprehensible without such training. Moreover, he must do so without simplifying to the point at which misleading conclusions might easily be drawn.

This dilemma is brought into sharpest focus when the "why" of something is to be explained. In some cases it is impossible to resolve in a reasonable way. When that has happened in this book I have simply explained "how" and have not said anything about "why." In no case, to the best of my knowledge, has accuracy been sacrificed in order to achieve simple presentation.

Such an approach seems justifiable in view of the book's purpose: to provide the interested layman with reliable, helpful guidance to the installation and operation of high-fidelity stereo music systems.

I am greatly indebted to Mr. Edgar Villchur, not only for specific suggestions in text and illustrations, but for collaboration in planning the original outline of subject matter. Valuable data and suggestions were supplied also by C. Victor Campos. Marie Spaulding handled typing, proofreading, and production, all with unfailing patience and competence. Arthur Seymour designed the book literally from cover to cover, including preparation of the artwork between.

Grateful acknowledgment is here given to Dynaco, Inc., H. H. Scott, Inc., Electro-Sonic Laboratories, Inc., Bogen-Presto, Marantz Company, McIntosh Laboratory, Inc., and Sherwood Electronics Laboratories, Inc., for the loan of equipment shown in the photographs and illustrations.

Much of the material in Chapters 6 and 8 was published originally in *HiFi/Stereo Review,* and is reprinted with the kind permission of that magazine.

1.

HIGH FIDELITY

THE TERMS "hi-fi" and "high fidelity" mean, simply, reproduction of sound in a manner that is highly faithful to the original.

What makes a sound system genuinely high in fidelity? Briefly, all parts of the system must have low distortion (spurious additions to the sound); the ability to handle a wide range of sound frequencies (pitches) without giving greater or lesser emphasis to any section of the frequency range than to others; adequate dynamic range (contrast between loud and soft passages); and other factors.

There is a price limitation at the low end. At the present state of development, it is fairly safe to say that the simplest monaural high-fidelity record-playing system cannot be obtained for less than $200, at net prices. For a high-fidelity stereo record-playing system, the lower limit is about $300. But you can pay $2,000 for a standard phonograph console and not get as good sound.

MONAURAL HI-FI COMPONENTS

The parts of a high-fidelity system — the components — are most conveniently considered in four groups. First are the *signal sources:* those components which originate electrical impulses that are electronic counterparts of sound waves. Three types of signal-source components are used commonly in home systems. They are radio tuners, which select and amplify broadcast waves and then extract the sound intelligence from them; tape playback machines (which may be able to make tape recordings, too); and record players, which consist of a turntable, a tone arm, and a pickup cartridge. The cartridge is installed at the front of the tone arm and includes a needle or stylus which, following the groove irregularities of a record, generates a small electric current.

1

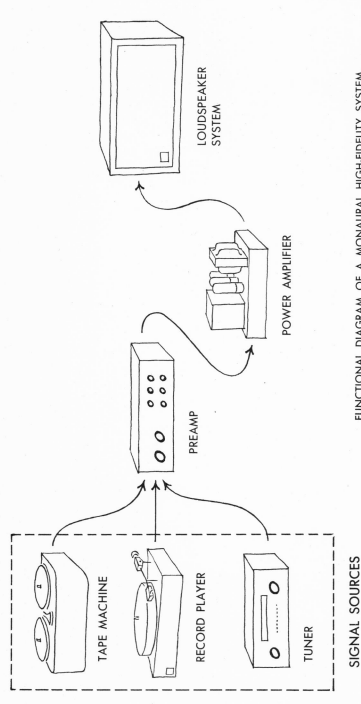

LOUDSPEAKER SYSTEM

POWER AMPLIFIER

PREAMP

SIGNAL SOURCES

TAPE MACHINE

RECORD PLAYER

TUNER

FUNCTIONAL DIAGRAM OF A MONAURAL HIGH-FIDELITY SYSTEM. THERE MAY BE ONLY ONE SIGNAL SOURCE TO BEGIN WITH; OTHERS MAY BE ADDED LATER. OFTEN THE PREAMP AND POWER AMPLIFIER ARE COMBINED IN ONE CASE. A TUNER MAY BE INCLUDED IN THE COMBINATION TOO.

Monaural record-playing system with FM-AM radio tuner. Speakers are in cabinet at right. The smaller photograph shows these cabinets with doors closed.

COURTESY NESHAMINY ELECTRONIC CORP. (JANSZEN)

A second general type of high-fidelity component, usually called for simplicity's sake a *preamplifier* or *preamp*, actually has several functions. All the signal sources are connected to the preamp, and it must have a switch to select whichever of them is to be used at the moment. It must have a circuit to equalize (put in proper relative balance according to frequency) the output of a pickup cartridge. Further, it must amplify (build up in strength) the extremely feeble electrical signal from the pickup to a level matching that from a tuner. This process is called preamplification — presumably because it precedes another step of amplification later on. If the tape player does not have built-in preamplification and equalization circuits, the preamp must perform these services for that component as well.

At least one volume control must be supplied on a preamp. Often there are other controls and switches on a monaural preamp which, while not absolutely essential, are convenient in varying degree; these include bass and treble tone controls, a switch for incorporating progressive bass boost at low settings of the main volume control (a "loudness compensation" or "contour" switch), and other devices of greater or lesser value.

The third type of component is the *power amplifier*. This accepts the output signal from a preamp, which is still at a very low power level, and builds it up to a level sufficiently high to drive a loudspeaker system. The amount of power amplification required is surprisingly high: from 2 millionths of a watt or less to at least 10 watts, usually more — an amplification of 5 to 50 million times.

The fourth component is the *loudspeaker system*, which converts the electrical output of the power amplifier into sound.

Some basic form of each of these components is necessary in even the most unpretentious table radio or portable phonograph. But the differences between a high-fidelity power amplifier, for example, and a power amplifier which must only make a loud noise, are nearly incredible. The former may weigh 40 pounds, use four or more tubes and several dozen other expensive parts, and will cost at least $50. The latter (as used in a portable phonograph) may weigh a few ounces, consist of one tube and a half-dozen other parts, and represent a dollar or so of the phonograph's cost.

This is not to say that only completely separate components can be really high in fidelity. Combinations of preamp and power amplifier, or tuner and preamp, are quite common and can be excellent. There are also good combinations of tuner, preamp, and power amplifier in one large unit. As a matter of fact, there is no reason why a superb complete high-fidelity system (with a separate but matching speaker complement) cannot be made, ready to plug in and play. This makes more sense from an engineering point of view than does assembling individual components bought separately.

2.

STEREO

Stereo on recorded tapes has been available for several years, but in that form it was able to attract the interest of relatively few devotees of high fidelity. Widespread awareness of home stereo sound began in 1958, following the introduction of a practical method of putting stereo on disc records and its adoption by the major record companies. One conclusion reached immediately by a great many people was that stereo made high-fidelity sound obsolete; that it was a replacement for and an improvement upon high fidelity. No doubt this conclusion was discreetly encouraged by some segments of the phonograph industry. It is a common misconception even now.

In a monaural system all the sound or the electrical signal representing that sound is carried in one information channel. No matter how many microphones may be used, the signals from all of them are mixed together before being recorded or broadcast. Once this happens, there is no way to separate the individual signals again; even if more than one amplifier or many speakers are used, they will always carry simultaneously the same composite signal.

The sound you hear from a monaural source will always be lacking in information about the original acoustic atmosphere. All of the sound of any particular frequency (which may involve several orchestral sections) appears to come from one particular location, even if you separate the individual parts of a speaker system. The "hall sound" is missing, or, at best, artificial.

A stereo system, on the other hand, makes use of two completely separate (although related and synchronized) channels from the microphones through to the speakers. In the simplest case, the sound picked up

5

A complete stereo high-fidelity system, installed in cabinets with louvered doors that can be closed to conceal and protect most of the components. The record player, which is the signal source used most often, is left at a convenient location and has a dust cover for protection.

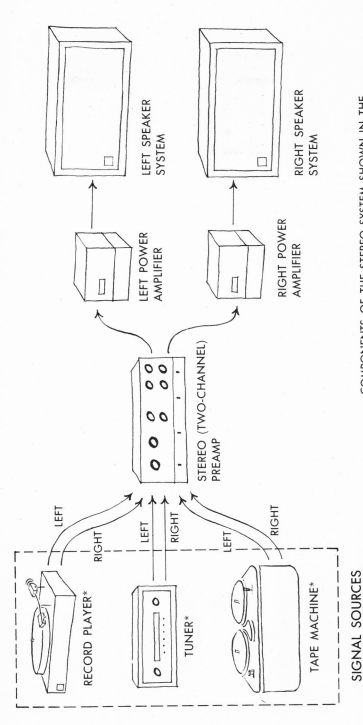

LEFT SPEAKER SYSTEM

RIGHT SPEAKER SYSTEM

LEFT POWER AMPLIFIER

RIGHT POWER AMPLIFIER

STEREO (TWO-CHANNEL) PREAMP

LEFT

RIGHT

LEFT

RIGHT

LEFT

RIGHT

RECORD PLAYER*

TUNER*

TAPE MACHINE*

SIGNAL SOURCES

*NOTE: SOME SIGNAL SOURCES MAY BE MONAURAL (SINGLE-CHANNEL)

COMPONENTS OF THE STEREO SYSTEM SHOWN IN THE ACCOMPANYING PICTURES. AS IN A MONAURAL SYSTEM, THERE MAY BE ONLY ONE SIGNAL SOURCE.

by a left-hand microphone is reproduced by the left-hand speaker at the same time that the sound picked up by a right-hand microphone is reproduced by the right-hand speaker. The difference in sound intensity received by the two mikes from a particular section of the orchestra, and the minute differences in the arrival time of the sound at the two microphone locations, are reproduced intact by the two speaker systems. Consequently there is reproduced in the space between the speakers a sound *field* similar in many ways to the complex sound field which existed between the two microphones.

A listener to a well-adjusted stereo system hears all the individual sections of a large orchestra or a small ensemble in proper spatial orientation. This is the most dramatic attribute of stereo, perhaps, but it is the least important in itself. The directional clues permit operation of the listener's binaural hearing faculty, which enables him to concentrate on any particular melodic line or lines — to observe the musical fabric, as it were. And the more accurate reproduction of the original acoustic environment gives a sense of realism that cannot be duplicated in a monaural recording.

It has been said that monaural sound reproduction brings the performance to the listener's living room; while stereo, in bringing the listener to the performance, frees him of his living room's acoustical limitations.

Essentially, then, a stereo system is two separate monaural systems operating at the same time and carrying slightly different sound signals. It should be evident that whatever advantages high fidelity has in a monaural system will apply with equal force in a stereo system. To put it another way, a poor phonograph will sound just as bad in an up-to-date stereo version.

3.

STEREO HI-FI COMPONENTS

RᴇQᴜɪʀᴇᴅ for a stereo system are two preamps, two power amplifiers, and two speaker systems, in addition to whatever stereo signal sources you select.

STEREO SIGNAL SOURCES

The two stereo channels are engraved on a disc record individually in each wall of the V-shaped groove. A stereo pickup cartridge is needed to sense these different wall shapes and convert the information to two stereo electrical signals. Only one tone arm and one turntable are required.

Some FM stations are now broadcasting stereo programs over a single transmitter. To receive them in stereo you must have either a stereo FM tuner, or an FM tuner with a "multiplex" output circuit and a separate multiplex adapter of the proper type.

A stereo tape has either one or two pairs of channels (tracks) recorded across the width of the tape, and the tape machine has a dual pickup head to sense these pairs of tracks. The latest machines will play both two-track and four-track tapes; older machines, unless converted, will play only two-track tapes. Any stereo tape machine, of course, has two signal output circuits for connection to your stereo preamps.

STEREO PREAMPS AND AMPLIFIERS

A stereo preamp contains two complete preamps in one case. Each of the preamps may have its own control knobs or the controls may be ganged — that is, one knob may operate the controls simultaneously for both the left-channel and right-channel sections. There are many variations and combinations of control systems; usually at least the selector switches, that

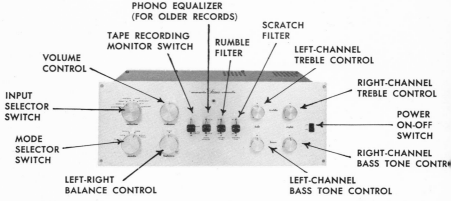

PHONO EQUALIZER
(FOR OLDER RECORDS)

TAPE RECORDING
MONITOR SWITCH

RUMBLE
FILTER

SCRATCH
FILTER

LEFT-CHANNEL
TREBLE CONTROL

VOLUME
CONTROL

RIGHT-CHANNEL
TREBLE CONTROL

INPUT
SELECTOR
SWITCH

POWER
ON-OFF
SWITCH

MODE
SELECTOR
SWITCH

RIGHT-CHANNEL
BASS TONE CONTROL

LEFT-RIGHT
BALANCE CONTROL

LEFT-CHANNEL
BASS TONE CONTROL

Controls provided on a stereo preamp. All except the tone controls, on the right, are ganged — that is, they affect both stereo channels simultaneously.

A stereo power amplifier: two complete power amplifiers in one case. Dual inputs are at center. Large sockets are for supplying power to a pair of monaural preamps if they require it. Switch at left of center converts unit to a monaural high-power amplifier. Output terminals are at rear.

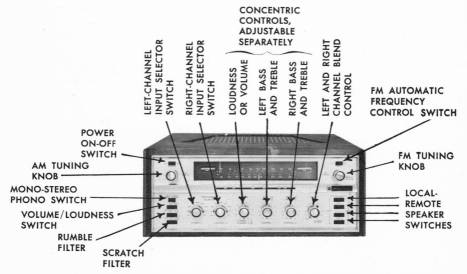

CONCENTRIC
CONTROLS,
ADJUSTABLE
SEPARATELY

LEFT-CHANNEL
INPUT SELECTOR
SWITCH

RIGHT-CHANNEL
INPUT SELECTOR
SWITCH

LOUDNESS
OR VOLUME

LEFT BASS
AND TREBLE

RIGHT BASS
AND TREBLE

LEFT AND RIGHT
CHANNEL BLEND
CONTROL

FM AUTOMATIC
FREQUENCY
CONTROL SWITCH

POWER
ON-OFF
SWITCH

FM TUNING
KNOB

AM TUNING
KNOB

MONO-STEREO
PHONO SWITCH

LOCAL-
REMOTE

VOLUME/LOUDNESS
SWITCH

SPEAKER
SWITCHES

RUMBLE
FILTER

SCRATCH
FILTER

This is a stereo FM-AM multiplex tuner, stereo preamp, and stereo power amplifier, all in one case. Although control arrangement differs from that of the stereo preamp shown nearby, it provides for essentially the same modes of operation.

select which of the signal sources are to be heard, are ganged.

In addition to the controls listed previously for monaural preamps, there are controls and switches required specifically for stereo functions. For example, there may be a channel-reverse switch (left-channel input to right-channel power amplifier, and vice versa). This is often part of a function or mode switch (with a choice of stereo normal, stereo reverse, left-channel monaural input to both output circuits, right-channel input to both output circuits, or both input channels mixed and fed to both output circuits). A balance control, which adjusts the *relative* volume of the two channels, is usually supplied. Sometimes there are other controls as well. If two monaural-type preamps are used, a stereo adapter containing these special stereo controls is a virtual necessity.

In the same way, the two power amplifiers are often combined in one chassis. It is fairly common, particularly in less expensive hi-fi systems, to find a dual preamp and dual power amplifiers all in one case. There are even a few such combinations which include a tuner or dual tuners.

It should be mentioned that monaural records can be played on a stereo system with excellent — although definitely monaural — results. (The reverse is not true: do not try to play stereo records with a monaural pickup cartridge.) A single tuner or any other monaural source can be connected to one of the stereo preamp inputs and played, by setting the function selector switch to the appropriate position, through both channels of the system. Alternatively a "Y" connector cable can be used to feed a monaural source to both stereo channels. Again, the sound will be two-speaker monaural.

CHOOSING YOUR COMPONENTS

This booklet is not intended to be a buying guide to specific brands of high-fidelity products. For such guidance you should consider information from a number of sources, and resolve any conflicts according to your own best judgment.

Dealers in high-fidelity components — like all dealers — are highly variable in their fidelity to customers' interests. Many are not only well

versed in the good and bad features of the equipment they sell, but are honestly concerned to see that customers get the best products for their needs. Others, on the other hand, have a tendency to steer customers to components whose manufacturers have the biggest dealer discounts or offer special sales incentives, whether or not these components represent good value to a customer.

Unless you are certain that you have a dealer of the first kind, you should look with suspicion on insistent attempts to steer you towards one brand or to switch you away from the brand you ask for. You should look for an unhurried, impartial demonstration of the components in which you are interested and in competing brands if you ask to hear them. And when listening comparatively, insist that the loudness be adjusted to equal levels for the comparison tests.

If the dealer will cooperate in permitting you to listen in your home to the units you have tentatively chosen (some dealers will do so), you can then be sure that they will be satisfactory before actually making a final choice.

Records can be helpful in evaluating high-fidelity equipment if you can be sure of what is on the records. Pickup cartridges and loudspeaker systems, in particular, can be judged by listening for the most natural string tone on a record like Vivaldi's *The Four Seasons* (Vanguard BGS 5001). Harshness and resonances in either component will be revealed clearly in comparison with units of superior quality.

Any good piano recording provides a tough test for a turntable. Listen for wavering pitch on sustained chords, and for fluttery effects in the middle register. In silent grooves of the record there should be no growling, very low-pitched background noise.

For testing the general excellence of an entire sound system, a well-recorded selection of chorus and orchestra is a good choice. One such is the beginning of side one of *Balshazzar's Feast* (Angel S 35681). When using this to make comparison tests, listen for best differentiation of the choral voices (you should be able to understand the words easily). Systems with smoothly extended high-frequency response will make the sibilants sound like *s*, as they should, rather than like *sh*. And the bass entrance on this record should reveal a truly flat, extended bass range in comparison with a falsely resonant one.

Magazines which specialize in music and audio subjects publish reports of tests on various high-fidelity components. Despite their best efforts to be honest and impartial in such reports, however, it is extremely awkward for magazines to be openly critical of their advertisers' products. The result is that the reports are often helpful, but to a limited degree; the temptation to rate all components as "best yet" (or at least to gloss over serious imperfections) is very powerful.

The reports of general testing organizations whose publications do not carry advertising usually can be relied on to be free of bias. But even these reports vary in reliability according to the skill of the engineers who obtain and interpret test data on which the reports are based. Such variation exists in reports of the same organization.

Audio shows which are held in large cities offer an opportunity to see and hear new products, and to make a preliminary screening of possible choices. Often the rooms or booths at these shows are crowded and do not even come close in acoustic character to a home listening room. Further, the manufacturers of some quite good high-fidelity products conduct deplorable demonstrations, so that their products sound no better at audio shows than do inferior products. Consequently it is unwise to make a final decision for or against any component simply on the basis of what you hear at an audio show.

Some manufacturers maintain continuous demonstration rooms (not sales rooms) where their products can be heard. AR, for example, has AR Music Rooms on the West Balcony of Grand Central Station in New York City and on Brattle Street in Harvard Square, Cambridge, Massachusetts. At these rooms good music can be heard in an atmosphere similar to that of a living room, and an accurate idea can be obtained of what the manufacturer's products can sound like in ideal circumstances. Other companies that have showrooms are Magnavox, RCA, and Zenith.

Listeners at the AR Music Room in Grand Central Station, New York City. No sales are made here. Questions are answered if asked, but visitors are not approached by the attendants.

There is a lot of nonsense spoken and written about high-fidelity components, but possibly the most ridiculous eyewash of all is the statement that loudspeaker systems cannot or should not be tested in an objective way. The alternative is obvious: pick your loudspeaker on the basis of its tonal quality, in the same way that you would choose a piano or violin — or a harmonica. Now, if you consider a loudspeaker to be a musical instrument, in the sense that it is meant to create unique sounds that do not necessarily have much similarity to the stimulus (the recording of the original sounds), then this viewpoint is a valid one. But if you subscribe to it you put the loudspeaker manufacturer in competition with Steinway, Stradivarius, and Hohner, and you never will be able to hear these instruments as they really sound except in the concert hall.

On the other hand, if you accept the premise that a loudspeaker system should *reproduce* sounds as accurately as possible, without adding to them or subtracting from them or changing them in any way, then the question of individual taste in loudspeaker "tonal quality" disappears. There is left only one criterion: how accurately the original sound is reproduced. If there is any subjective choice involved, it must legitimately be concerned only with what kind of departure from perfect reproduction is least objectionable, and with such unrelated matters as cabinet size, style, cost, and so on.

Admittedly it is difficult to remember with precision the sound of live instruments and voices. This does not change the criterion, however; if

Members of The Fine Arts Quartet listening to a playback of recorded sections of the works they will perform in live-vs.-recorded concerts. These recordings were made out of doors in order to avoid room reverberation. Thus the loudspeaker-reproduced parts of the music and the sections played live by the Quartet are on an equal basis in a concert hall: both are colored only once, and in the same way, by the acoustic atmosphere of the hall.

A live-vs.-recorded demonstration, in which the Fine Arts Quartet alternated with a recording of themselves playing the same works. Switches were made from one to the other at irregular intervals. (This demonstration was produced by Acoustic Research and Dynakit. G. A. Briggs of Wharfedale has sponsored similar shows.)

anything, it is an argument for more frequent attendance at live performances. One simple and completely objective test for any high-fidelity system is a live-vs.-recorded concert, in which musicians perform alternately with reproduced sections of the same music. Some demonstrations are so nearly perfect that the changes from live to loudspeaker-reproduced sections cannot be detected by most listeners. It is regrettable that concerts of this kind are not given more frequently than they are, preferably with industry sponsorship. This is a most rigorous and demanding test of quality, however, and only a few individual manufacturers have attempted it. It is significant that Consumers' Union (one of the most respected of the independent testing organizations) has announced that it uses this technique for the evaluation of loudspeaker systems.

Finally, there is the reputation of the manufacturer, as reflected in the opinions of present owners of his products, which should be taken into account. You can learn from the man who owns one how a component stands up in use, how the manufacturer responds to a need for service, and whether or not the initial promise has become long-term satisfaction.

If you have even a moderate interest in mechanical things you should look into the many kits which are available with simple and accurate assembly instructions.

4.

CABLES AND PLUGS

O NE REASON why people tend to be wary of component high-fidelity systems is a suspicion that it takes an engineer to install one and wire it together properly. This simply isn't so.

With only rare exceptions, interconnecting the parts of a high-fidelity system involves nothing more than inserting a few plugs into the right sockets, and attaching a few wires to screw terminals or knurled-nut binding posts. Whatever cables you need are either supplied with the components or can be bought ready-made. Wires for speaker connection can be made easily from TV antenna wire or common lamp cord, available by the foot from hardware stores.

AC POWER CONNECTIONS

All components in the system excepting the speakers and, possibly, a stereo adapter, must be connected to an AC power outlet. Usually the preamp has enough AC outlets on its back panel to accommodate the line-cord plugs from the other components. In such a case only the preamp must be plugged into a wall outlet.

Some of the preamp's AC outlets may be controlled by the front-panel on-off switch and some may not be. Since the only other AC-powered components used every time the system is turned on are the power amplifiers, their AC line cords should be plugged into the switched preamp AC outlets if there is a choice in the matter. Then the power amplifier on-off switches can be left in the "on" positions, and they will be turned on and off with the preamp.

The turntable should be plugged into an *unswitched* AC outlet, so that it must be turned on and off by its own switch. This may prevent flat spots on rubber-rimmed idler wheels left engaged accidentally while at rest. It

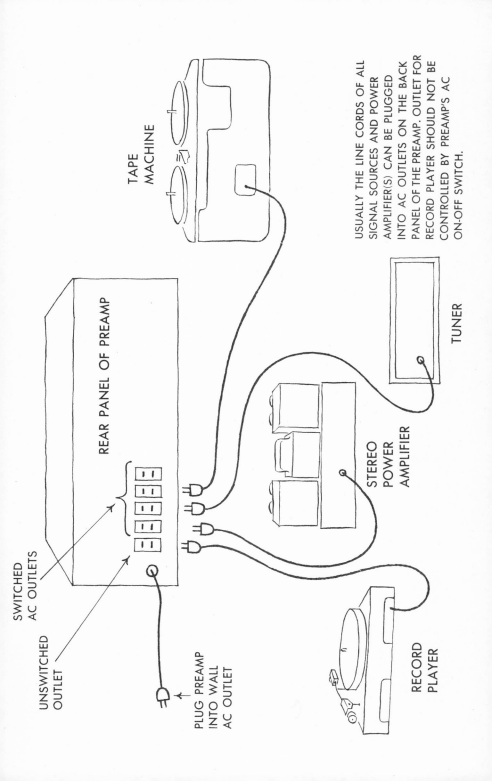

TAPE MACHINE

REAR PANEL OF PREAMP

SWITCHED AC OUTLETS

UNSWITCHED OUTLET

PLUG PREAMP INTO WALL AC OUTLET

STEREO POWER AMPLIFIER

TUNER

RECORD PLAYER

USUALLY THE LINE CORDS OF ALL SIGNAL SOURCES AND POWER AMPLIFIER(S) CAN BE PLUGGED INTO AC OUTLETS ON THE BACK PANEL OF THE PREAMP. OUTLET FOR RECORD PLAYER SHOULD NOT BE CONTROLLED BY PREAMP'S AC ON-OFF SWITCH.

doesn't matter much whether or not the other components are connected to preamp-switched power outlets or not; they all are supplied with on-off switches of their own.

Even when a dual-channel stereo preamp and dual power amplifier are combined on one chassis, there usually are auxiliary AC power outlets on the back panel for the signal-source components. If not, a short extension cord with a multiple-outlet termination can be put to good use.

If a loudspeaker system is plugged into an AC house-current outlet it will receive something like 1,000 watts at 60 cycles per second. The exact amount will vary with the speaker system's impedance but, in any case, it is sure to destroy the speaker almost instantly. To avoid that possibility *never, for any reason whatever,* attach a line-cord plug to a speaker system cable. Someone, sometime, will plug it into an AC outlet if you do.

FM ANTENNAS

An FM tuner (or the FM section of an AM/FM tuner) requires an antenna of some sort. A good rooftop antenna is a practical necessity for urban apartment buildings with steel framework. In fringe reception areas, only a broadband Yagi antenna will do a good enough job. In the suburbs of large metropolitan areas a simple FM antenna installed in the attic usually works well. Still simpler, and satisfactory in favorable reception areas, is the twin-lead antenna shown in the diagram. This can be stapled

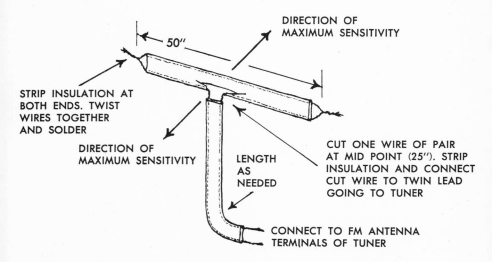

How to make a simple FM antenna which is very effective in favorable receiving locations.

inside a closet, on the back of a cabinet holding high-fidelity equipment, along a baseboard moulding, or in any convenient location so long as it isn't very close to large bodies of metal.

No matter which kind of antenna installation may be used, the antenna should be oriented so that its most sensitive angle corresponds with the direction of most of the FM transmitters in the area. This varies with the particular type of antenna; your dealer will be able to help you on this point. The twin-lead antenna is equally sensitive in the two directions marked in the diagram (broadside to its horizontal section).

Except for special cases best handled by a professional antenna installation man, all FM antennas are connected to tuners with standard 300-ohm twin lead — the kind used for TV installations. The same precautions as in TV apply, too: the run from the antenna should be as short and as vertical as practical; the line should be supported away from the house by stand-off insulators; a lightning protector should be installed on an outside antenna; and the line should not run along close to metallic objects such as pipes or rain gutters and downspouts. Incidentally, antenna switches are available at nearly any TV service store which can be used to switch an antenna between a TV set and an FM tuner. A single antenna thus can serve very well for both.

No external antenna is needed for AM reception, except in extreme fringe areas. During the daytime an AM tuner's built-in antenna is adequate in most cases. At night, if the receiving location is far enough away from the desired station to need an external antenna, the reception is likely to be so badly disturbed by fading and interference that it would be far more satisfactory to play records. If the tuner you buy doesn't have a built-in AM antenna, the instruction book will tell you how to install an external one or the connections you must make to use the FM antenna for AM also.

SIGNAL INTERCONNECTIONS

Signal connections to be made among the components of a stereo system are indicated on the following page. Connections from all the signal-source components to the preamp, and from the preamp to the power amplifiers, must be made with shielded phono cable. The two power amplifiers are shown separated by a dashed line, which indicates that they may be completely separate units or combined on one chassis; the connections are the same in either case. There is a similar dashed line, with a similar meaning, separating the two preamp sections.

If the two preamplifiers are separate components, however, there will be connections between them and a stereo adapter unit. These connections are not shown because they depend on the specific type of adapter used. Instructions supplied with the adapter should be followed. Shielded phono

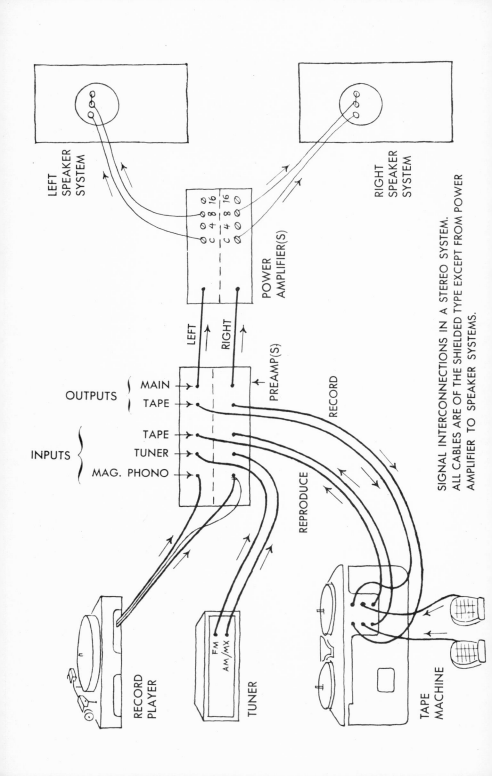

LEFT SPEAKER SYSTEM

RIGHT SPEAKER SYSTEM

POWER AMPLIFIER(S)

16 8 4 C
16 8 4 C

LEFT

RIGHT

PREAMP(S)

OUTPUTS { MAIN
TAPE

INPUTS { TAPE
TUNER
MAG. PHONO

RECORD

REPRODUCE

RECORD PLAYER

TUNER

FM
AM/MX

TAPE MACHINE

SIGNAL INTERCONNECTIONS IN A STEREO SYSTEM. ALL CABLES ARE OF THE SHIELDED TYPE EXCEPT FROM POWER AMPLIFIER TO SPEAKER SYSTEMS.

cables will be required in any case.

Finally, connections *from* the preamp *to* the tape machine, if the tape machine records as well as plays tapes, are made with shielded phono cable.

Two monaural preamps, used for stereo with a stereo adapter (small box at left).

Proper observance must be made throughout the stereo system of channel markings. The left-hand or channel A preamp output should be connected to the left-hand power amplifier input, the left-hand power amplifier output terminals should be connected to the left-hand speaker, and so on. Wiring instructions for the pickup arm and cartridge will indicate which wires are for the left-hand channel. The tape recorder input and output jacks will be labeled to indicate which is left and right (or channel A and channel B). It is common practice to connect the FM section of a stereo tuner to the left-hand radio input on the preamp, and the AM section or an FM multiplex source to the right-hand input on the preamp. It is conventional also to connect monaural sources to left-hand preamp inputs.

Rear panel of a stereo preamp. This one has provision for more than the usual variety of signal sources, in addition to multiple output circuits. "Trim" adjustments are for balancing low-frequency performance of speaker systems.

Obviously, if a stereo amplifier and preamp are all combined in one case, it will not be necessary to make any connections between them. If a tuner is included on the same chassis, that is another pair of connections you don't have to make. And if you have a combined tuner and stereo preamp, the connections between the tuner and preamp are built in, but you'll have to make them between the preamp sections of the unit and the power amplifiers.

Shielded phono cable consists of an inner conductor, which is the core of the cable; a layer of insulation surrounding that; a braided shield, which is the outer conductor; and, outside the shield, another layer of insulating material.

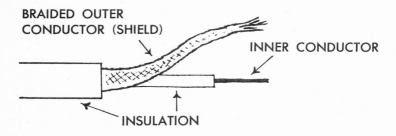

BRAIDED OUTER
CONDUCTOR (SHIELD)

INNER CONDUCTOR

INSULATION

SHIELDED PHONO CABLE

The standard type of connector used in high-fidelity systems is known as the *RCA phono plug and jack.* Shielded cables are fitted at each end with a plug, which is inserted into the appropriate jack on the preamp, amplifier, or other component. The jacks are clearly labeled if there are more than one. On a stereo preamp, for example, the jacks will be separated

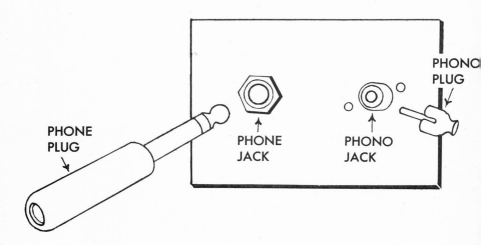

PHONO
PLUG

PHONE
PLUG

PHONE
JACK

PHONO
JACK

for "Left Channel" (or "Channel A") and "Right Channel" (or "Channel B"). They will be grouped under "Inputs" (the various signal sources) and "Outputs" (Power amp, Tape recorder).

Often the appropriate cables are supplied with the components by the manufacturers. If you aren't that lucky you can buy shielded phono cables already made up in four, six, or eight-foot lengths, with appropriate plugs attached, at most stores and mail-order houses handling high-fidelity equipment. Adapters and couplers (to make longer cables from two or more short ones) are available also. We suggest that you avoid making up your own shielded cables.

One pair of shielded cables you may not be able to avoid soldering, if you mounted your own pickup arm, are those from the arm to the preamp. But you can make the job easier by getting ready-made cables of the proper length with an RCA phono jack at one end and the other end simply stripped of insulation, ready for attachment to the terminal board under the turntable base. Specific connections vary at this point; follow the pickup arm manufacturer's recommendations. (Some arms now are supplied complete with cables and plugs.) Should you have hum trouble the suggestions in a later chapter may be helpful.

If you have a tape machine which can record as well as play tapes, it probably has two kinds of input circuits. One pair of inputs will be labeled "Mike" or "Microphone" and its purpose is, of course, to permit you to make live recordings with a pair of microphones. If the microphones are supplied with the machine, they will have the plugs of the proper kind attached. If the microphones are not supplied, your machine is likely to have the potential for making live recordings of high quality. You'll need good microphones for that, and more detailed information on how to hook them up and use them, than this booklet can attempt to give you.

The other pair of tape recorder input jacks may be marked "Hi-Level In," "Preamp In," or something similar. Connecting these jacks via shielded cables to the "Tape Out" or "To Tape Rec" jacks on your preamp enables you to record whatever other source—tuner or disc record—is being played on the main system.

Microphone input jacks on a tape machine usually are not RCA phono jacks, but *phone* jacks. Both types are illustrated herewith. The other tape machine input and output jacks may be of either type. It is possible, then, that the shielded phono cables connecting the tape machine and preamp may have to be fitted with phone plugs at one end and RCA phono plugs at the other. These also are available ready-made.

SPEAKER CONNECTIONS

Connections from the power amplifiers to the speaker systems may be made with TV antenna twin lead, which fits nicely under carpets, pro-

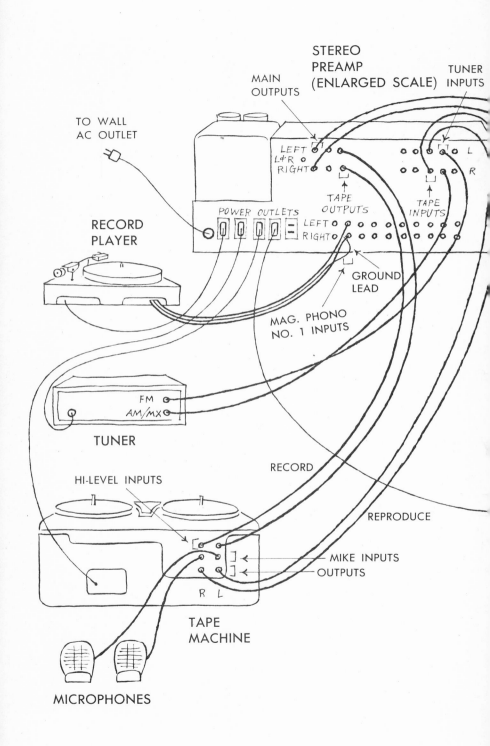

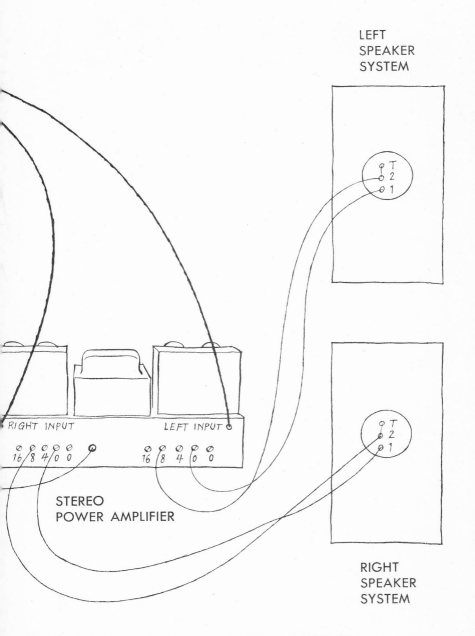

LEFT
SPEAKER
SYSTEM

T
2
1

RIGHT INPUT

LEFT INPUT

16 8 4 0 0

16 8 4 0 0

T
2
1

STEREO
POWER AMPLIFIER

RIGHT
SPEAKER
SYSTEM

PICTORIAL REPRESENTATION OF AC AND SIGNAL WIRING FOR A
COMPLETE STEREO SYSTEM. AC POWER CONNECTIONS ARE INDICATED
BY LIGHT LINES, SIGNAL WIRING BY HEAVY LINES.

A complete stereo record-playing system. Key to wiring shown:

1. Cable from amplifier to left channel speaker

2. Cable from amplifier to right channel speaker

3. Dual cable from turntable to amplifier

4. Turntable power cord (plugs into amplifier)

5. Main power cord (plugs into wall outlet)

6. Sockets for FM tuner cable

These cables are supplied with the components, except for the speaker wires. The latter can be of any desired length and are made from ordinary lamp cord.

Components consist of two AR-4 speaker systems, Dyna SCA-35 integrated amplifier, AR turntable with arm, and Shure M7-N21D pickup cartridge.

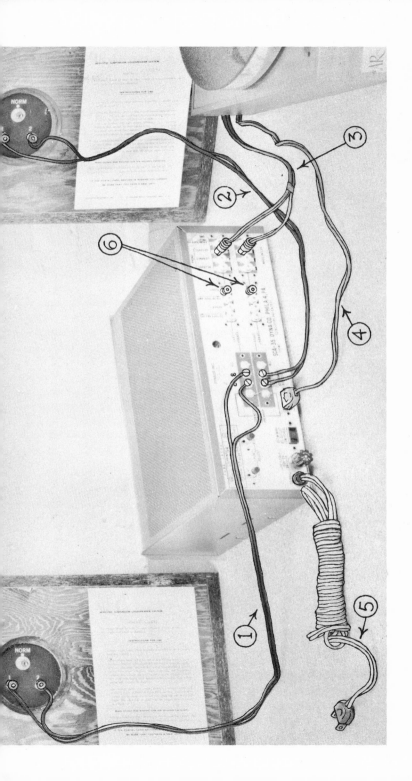

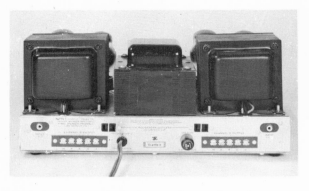

Rear view of a stereo power amplifier. Channel A inputs and outputs correspond to "left" orientation; channel B, to "right."

vided the speakers are not more than 15 to 20 feet away from the amplifiers. When the distance is greater than this you can use ordinary lamp wire or "zip cord". Lamp wire is made in several colors, so you can make this wiring less conspicuous by choosing a color to match the baseboards.

If that idea doesn't appeal to you either, you can run the wiring under the floor from the amplifier location to the speaker locations. An even more elegant (but more expensive) solution is to have your electrician install in-the-wall wiring via special wall outlets or jacks. He can use either BX cable or indoor plastic sheathed cable, and can install pairs of outlets wherever you may want to connect speakers to the high-fidelity system. Wires from the speakers should be fitted with matching plugs. Make absolutely certain he understands that the outlets and plugs must not be able to get mixed up with house-current outlets and plugs.

Power amplifiers have screw-type output terminals. Ordinarily there will be four terminals for each amplifier section, marked "O" or "C", "4", "8", and "16". One wire of the pair going to a speaker system should be connected to the "O" or "C" terminal. The other wire should be connected to whichever amplifier terminal corresponds to the impedance rating for the speaker system (4, 8, or 16 ohms).

5.

PHYSICAL INSTALLATION

H IGH FIDELITY components can be set up on a table or shelf, in a closet, on bookshelves or in a wall cabinet, in an antique chest or dry sink, or even in a ready-made cabinet bought for them (you can assemble your own console phonograph if you want to). There are only a few precautions to observe when making the installation.

GENERAL RULES

First, provide adequate ventilation. This is an unequivocal requirement for power amplifiers, tuners, and tape machines, and to a lesser extent for preamps. No ventilation is needed for turntables and speaker systems.

For components which need ventilation, air must be allowed free entry at the bottom of the space in which they are enclosed, and it must be permitted to escape somewhere at the top of the space.

Some components have small legs or rubber or plastic feet, and punched vent holes in the bottom of the chassis or case. Do not remove the feet, and do not put such components on pads of felt or foam rubber; doing so will restrict the flow of cool air into the holes. If a heat-producing component has a shelf directly over it and closer than eight inches, it is wise to line the bottom of that shelf with Fiberglas insulation to prevent excessive heat absorption.

Turntable, tape machine, tuner, and preamp should all be reasonably close to one another and easily accessible. This is mostly for the sake of convenience. If you have a good pickup cartridge of the magnetic type, you should be able to install the turntable at least six feet away from the preamp, if necessary, without significant deterioration of performance. The same is true of most tuners and tape machines.

If a tape machine does *not* have built-in playback preamplifiers, how-

Components of a high-fidelity sound system can be arranged in any number of ways, limited only by the imagination of the installer.

ever, it should not be placed more than three feet or so from the preamp because the connecting cables between the two components must be short.

Power amplifiers need not be readily accessible and, with just about any preamp now being made, can be 20 feet or more from the preamp. You can put the speaker systems 50 feet or more away from the power amplifier.

Usually only the turntable must be shock-mounted. It is advisable to buy the optional base offered by most turntable manufacturers if it has springs designed for use with that particular turntable. If the base you elect to use does not have shock mounts, and if these are not built into the turntable itself, you can buy shock-mount springs at most stores that sell high-fidelity components.

Also generally available are telescopic pull-out slides or runners for turntable bases. They are particularly convenient when the turntable must be installed with little overhead clearance or towards the bottom of a cabinet. You can mount a tape machine in the same way if you bolt the machine to a wooden platform.

A parenthetical but most important note is necessary at this point. *Read the instruction sheets or booklets carefully* that are supplied with your equipment. One of your components may require an exception to the rules given in this booklet, which are necessarily general in nature. If the manufacturer's instructions disagree with those given here, follow his.

THE TONE ARM AND CARTRIDGE

It used to be true that integral turntable-and-arm combinations (record players) were compromise affairs designed to fill the quality gap between record changers, on the one hand, and turntables and individual arms, on the other. Neither the arm nor the table of such a record player was likely

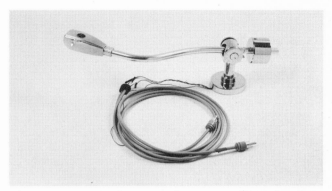

A tone arm meant for use with any turntable and pickup cartridge. Cables are supplied.

to be especially good. There is no reason why they cannot be as good or better than individual units, however, and now there are some really excellent ones. At least one (manufactured by AR, Inc.) is equipped with a base, dust cover, stylus force gauge, and cartridge overhang template, and has cables and line cord attached.

Turntable, base, and wired tone arm combination. This unit is ready to play after pickup cartridge is installed in removable cartridge shell.

*A turntable and base of one manufac-
turer combined with an integrated tone
arm and pickup cartridge of another.*

Whether you buy a record player or the turntable and arm separately, your dealer probably will install the pickup cartridge in the arm if you ask him to. There may be a small extra charge for this. Some dealers will mount an arm on a turntable if you buy both at the same time. Should you find it necessary to mount a tone arm and/or install a pickup cartridge yourself, the directions in Appendix A (p. 87) should be helpful.

CHECKING NEEDLE ALIGNMENT

Install the cartridge and stylus. Put a small mirror (such as might be found in a lady's purse) on the turntable platen, reflecting side up, and put the arm in record-playing position with the stylus resting on the mirror. With the cartridge viewed head-on, the reflection of the stylus should be perfectly in symmetrical alignment with the stylus itself; if it is not, either the arm, the cartridge, or the stylus is canted slightly.

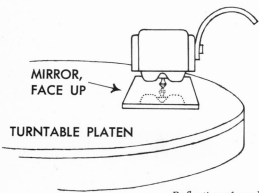

MIRROR,
FACE UP →

TURNTABLE PLATEN

*Reflection of needle in mirror should be aligned
with the needle itself.*

In order to obtain optimal performance the stylus *must* be laterally perpendicular to the record surface (that is, perpendicular when viewed from the front). Should you find that it *is* canted slightly, remove the cartridge carefully (or the plug-in head in which it is installed) and examine it. If the stylus is canted with respect to the cartridge body, it is defective and should be repaired or replaced. If the stylus itself seems all right, the trouble evidently is a slightly misaligned arm or cartridge mounting shell.

Except for integral arm/cartridge combinations, cartridge misalignment can be corrected easily by putting a thin paper or cardboard shim between the cartridge body and the mounting shell, at one mounting screw or the other depending on which way the cartridge is canted. If the cartridge cannot be removed from its shell, an alignment shim can be put under one side of the arm base, between the base and the turntable mounting board.

SETTING STYLUS FORCE

Stylus force is the downward force the needle applies to a record, measured in grams (about 28 grams equals one ounce).

It is very important that stylus force be correct. If it is too light, the needle will not trace the record groove properly; if it is too heavy, the needle suspension may be damaged. Record wear is accelerated by a stylus force either too light or too heavy. The recommendation of the pickup cartridge manufacturer should be followed.

The best kind of stylus-force gauge is one that can be read while the stylus is at record-playing height. There are many good ones; perhaps the simplest and most trouble-free are of the beam-balance type illustrated.

Beam balance type of needle force gauge. Measurement with any type of gauge should be made with needle at or very close to record-playing height.

Pennies or other weights in the amount specified for a given force are stacked on one end of the "beam." Towards the center, there is some sort of a fulcrum. The needle is put in a small depression at the other end of the beam and the stylus force is adjusted until the weights are balanced.

Stylus force is set with some arms simply by adjusting the counterweight at the back so that it doesn't quite balance out the weight of the cartridge at the front. In other words, the residual imbalance of the arm is used to establish the required stylus force.

With what are known as balanced arms, the stylus force is obtained by means of a spring. First the spring tension is reduced to zero, and the counterweight is adjusted so that the arm is as perfectly balanced about the vertical pivot as is possible. Then the spring tension is set for the desired stylus force.

One word of warning: don't rely on the stylus-force calibration scales, which may appear on the pickup arm, for an arm of either type. Accuracy is important, and an external gauge is far more likely to be accurate than the arm's rough calibrations.

Initially, the force should be set in the middle of the recommended range for the pickup cartridge you are using. If you should find later that there are crackling or fuzzy sounds when playing very loudly-recorded passages, you should reset the stylus force to a value at the high end of the recommended range; and if you can decrease the stylus force to the low end of the recommended range without audible distress on your loudest records, it is legitimate and advisable to do so, for the sake of decreased record wear.

POSITIONING LOUDSPEAKER SYSTEMS

When stereo first received nation-wide promotion it was thought that low frequencies contributed nothing to the stereo effect. For that reason there were marketed several loudspeaker systems in which the bass for both channels was combined and fed to one woofer; the middle-range and high frequencies were kept separate for the two channels, and reproduced by very small speakers. The expense of one woofer could thus be saved.

This was a laudable aim, but our experience has indicated that such systems are not completely satisfactory. Recently this impression has been confirmed by a long series of tests conducted by engineers of the General Electric Company.

Loudspeakers for stereo should be two full-range systems, spaced at least six feet apart. When it is practical, their spacing beyond this minimum should be determined by the size of the room in which they are used. The larger the room, the farther apart the speaker systems may be.

It is not true that there is only one small point within a room at which "you can get the full stereo effect." It *is* true, however, that the furnishings of most living rooms are already arranged with a concentration of seating facilities in one general area. If it is otherwise convenient, the loudspeakers should be put as far as possible from this area; both should be the same distance from the area and facing it; and they should be spaced apart by ½ to ¾ their distance from the center of the area, provided that speaker separation is at least six feet.

Many people believe that the most natural results are obtained when the speaker systems are on tables, stands, or bookshelves about 30 inches from the floor (about seated ear-level height), and that seems reasonable. The speakers don't have to be against the same wall — they may be put close to adjacent walls separated by a corner or, if the room is unusually long and narrow, on opposite walls near the same end of the room, turned to face the listening area.

The bass is reinforced for any speaker system when it is situated in a corner of the room. You might get too much reinforcement if you put both speaker systems in corners but, when they are not put on the floor, corner-mounting one of the systems may be beneficial and certainly is worth trying.

All the contradictory material that has been written on the subject notwithstanding, speaker placement seems to us to be not very critical from the point of view of the stereo effect. The general rules above can be stretched quite severely with excellent results, particularly when the loudspeakers have reasonably smooth response and good dispersion of high frequencies. Moreover, our experience has been that there is little merit in so-called "center-channel" auxiliary speakers. There will be no "hole in the middle" that requires filling if the stereo system is a good one. The only exceptions may be a system in which the main speakers must be spaced farther apart than their distance to the center of the listening area, or when loudspeakers are used in a large auditorium.

In either stereo or monaural systems, speakers may sound much better when mounted in one part of a room than in another, because of the way they stimulate the acoustical environment of the room. A long, hall-shaped room, for example, may encourage boomy, over-reverberant sound when the speakers face the long dimension. Since stereo frees the listener to some extent from the acoustical environment of his own listening room, speaker placement is more critical in monaural systems, and is worth experimenting with.

A more extended discussion of listening-room acoustics is given in the following chapter.

SOME ILLUSTRATIONS

THERE HAVE been shown a few actual high-fidelity equipment installations in earlier chapters. Some more examples appear on the following pages.

These photographs are meant to show possibilities of approach, from the simplest to the most elaborate, and are not represented as being perfect in all respects. Each of the installations does have at least one unusually good feature, however, and among them you may find an idea or two for your own use.

Most of the photographs in the following section were obtained from the files of *High Fidelity* Magazine, whose generous cooperation is acknowledged gratefully.

Stereo installation in a playroom. A record changer and combined tuner-amplifier-preamp are in cabinets on the right; one stereo speaker system is mounted in the bookcase at the left, the other is recessed into the wall behind open cabinet door.

COURTESY BELL SOUND DIVISION

*Behind the tambour doors in the central section of this complete stereo system
are a record changer, a combined stereo tuner-preamp, a dual power amplifier,
and record storage space. Speaker systems are on separate matching bases at
the ends.*

Closet space is being put to good use here. The central section contains a tuner, stereo amplifier and preamp, a record player, and record storage shelves. Speakers are in grilled spaces above the end closets.

Loudspeakers are installed at opposite ends of the lower section of this corner built-in, with record changer, stereo preamp and amplifiers, and TV in the center. All electronic components (including the television set) are concealed when not in use.

COURTESY CUSTOM ELECTRONICS, INC., NEW ORLEANS

Another built-in system with doors to conceal components when they aren't being used. Record changer is on a sliding platform next to amplifier and pre-amp. Large speaker systems are in closets on both sides.

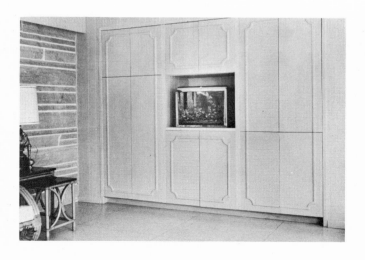

COURTESY KLH RESEARCH AND DEVELOPMENT CORPORATION

Although very simple, this monaural high-fidelity system should be as excellent in performance as it is efficient in its use of space. There are only three parts: a record-playing assembly, a monaural amplifier-preamp combination, and the speaker system. An improvement in sound might be had by raising the speaker off the floor.

41

6.

THE LISTENING ROOM

Much has been published on the problems of concert-hall acoustics. The celebrated difficulties at Lincoln Center's Philharmonic Hall, while of interest, are somewhat remote from the acoustic problems the average music listener must deal with in his own listening room. Yet the body of air that lies between the cone of the speaker and the ear of the listener *in his own home* has enormous potential for enhancing or impairing the quality of the sound his high-fidelity system produces. This potential is directly affected by physical factors capable of being predicted, measured, and—most important—controlled. This chapter discusses what the listening room's acoustic performance should be, and describes what can be done to obtain the performance desired.

Before we go further, a brief review of some basic acoustical concepts may be in order. A sound wave is generated by alternate compression and rarefaction of the air. As a loudspeaker cone moves forward, it compresses the air immediately in front of it. This "front" of increased air pressure spreads outward and away from the loudspeaker at the speed of sound—approximately 1,130 feet per second. Meanwhile, the loudspeaker cone reverses its motion, and by so doing creates a rarefaction. A front of decreased air pressure then spreads outward at the same speed. Thus, as the loudspeaker's cone moves alternately forward and backward, waves of compression and rarefaction are radiated into the room.

If the cone makes 100 to-and-fro motions every second, each compression wave will follow the preceding one at a time interval of $\frac{1}{100}$ second. In that interval each compression wave will travel $\frac{1}{100}$ of 1,130 feet, or 11.3 feet. (Rarefactions are separated by the same distance, of course.) The distance in air between a sound wave's corresponding parts is called its *wave length;* 11.3 feet, then, is the wave length of a sound wave of a frequency of 100 cycles per second (cps).

When a speaker cone makes 500 to-and-fro motions each second, a 500-cps sound wave is generated. Its wave length is 1,130 divided by 500, or 2¼ feet. A 40-cps frequency represents a sound-wave length of 1,130 divided by 40, or 28.2 feet. The lower the frequency of a sound wave, the greater its wave length. It is apparent that these low-frequency wave lengths approximate the dimensions of most living rooms.

ROOM RESONANCES

When a sound wave encounters an obstruction or meets a boundary—such as the wall of a room—part of the sound is reflected and part of it is absorbed. Both actions are important, for they determine how the room modifies or "shapes" the sound. For the moment, let us consider the reflected part of the sound.

Imagine a loudspeaker located at one end of a room 15 feet long, reproducing a frequency of 37.7 cps. The wave length is 1,130 divided by 37.7, or 30 feet—exactly twice the length of the room. A compression that travels the length of the room, is reflected from the end wall, and travels back to the speaker will arrive just in time to meet another compression being generated. It will reinforce that compression. In fact, the 37.7-cps tone might be uncomfortably loud at both ends of the room, because at those points the reflected sound and the direct sound are always in additive relationship. At the center of the room, however, the reflected compression wave coincides with the direct rarefaction wave, and there is cancellation rather than reinforcement. This is a so-called standing wave, or resonance, and is like any other acoustic resonance (as in a brass musical instrument or an organ pipe).

A room has standing-wave resonances at many frequencies, which are determined by the room dimensions. The number, frequency spacing, physical distribution, and severity of these standing waves are responsible for the acoustic character of the room.

Such room resonances are beneficial, if properly controlled, in two ways: first, they decrease the amount of acoustic power it is necessary to put into the room for a given loudness; second, they provide an acoustic environment without which music would sound quite unnatural. The room should not have a strong personality of its own. If it does, it can mask the desirable reverberative character of the concert hall which has been recorded along with the music, and thus decrease the illusion of reality. Such a room is likely to be unpleasant to live in, to say nothing of its effect on reproduced sound. But an overly "dead" room is almost as unpleasant in a different way, and reproduced music sounds just as unnatural in it, since experience leads us to expect to hear reflected sound in a room as well as direct sound. If all reflections are missing, even the recorded concert-hall reverberation cannot make up for the loss.

The trick is to strike the proper balance between an excessively live and a dull, dead room; to spread the room's resonant frequencies as evenly as possible; and to avoid exciting those standing waves that are harmful. When this is done the room reinforcement becomes fairly uniform for all frequencies, so that the tone color of complex musical sounds is preserved; the listening position within the room becomes less critical; and the room reverberation is at such a level that it provides minimum interference with the recorded reverberation but is not disturbingly absent. It is worth trying to approach this ideal for the same reasons that it is worth the expense to use high-fidelity speakers, amplifiers, and record-playing equipment.

OPTIMUM ROOM PROPORTIONS

The standing wave of lowest frequency for any room is found by dividing 565 by the *length* of the room in feet. (This gives the frequency at which the room is one-half wave length long.) For example, if the room length is 20 feet, the fundamental (lowest) resonant frequency is 565 divided by 20, or 28.2 cps. Standing waves occur also at all multiples of the room's fundamental length resonance. Similar sets of resonances exist for the width and height dimensions of the room.

At this point we can shift our attention from theory to practice. Since the frequencies at which room reinforcement occurs are determined by all the room dimensions, individually and in combination, how should these dimensions be related?

Let us consider a very bad listening room with dimensions of 10 by 10 by 10 feet. All three dimensions are the same; therefore, each dimension has the same first resonant frequency, the same second resonant frequency, and so on. This creates groups of three identical single-dimensional resonances at frequencies of 56.5 cps and at all multiples of that frequency.

This is the worst possible case. A number of resonances at the same frequency, isolated far from other resonant frequencies, produce very powerful reinforcement only at those frequencies and very little reinforcement between. Such a room would be thoroughly objectionable for music-listening purposes.

Only a little less objectionable is a room in which two dimensions are identical, or in which one dimension is an exact multiple of another.

The gap between the first and second resonant frequencies for each dimension is one octave. To obtain the best frequency distribution of standing waves, therefore, it seems logical to proportion the room dimensions so that the first resonances for length, width, and height are evenly spaced within one octave. It turns out that this is accomplished when the ratio of width to height is as the cube root of 2 (about 1.26) is to 1, and when length is related to width by the same ratio—in other words, when the three dimensions are related approximately as 1 to 1.25 to 1.6. A room 16 by 12½ feet, with a 10-foot ceiling, has these proportions.

Ideal proportions for a room, at least in the acoustic sense, can rarely be obtained except for relatively small rooms. In most practical circumstances the height is limited to 8 feet or less by the hard facts of economics. Following the 1¼-ratio rule, the width must be 10 feet and the length must be 12½ feet. The lowest standing-wave frequency is 45.2 cps; there are only two resonances below 70 cps.

From the point of view of sound reproduction only, there are at least two disadvantages in a room this small. First, there is little or no reinforcement of very low frequencies. This is not to say that frequencies below 45 cps cannot be generated in the room; they can be. But a speaker system has a difficult enough job producing these very low frequencies under favorable conditions, and if the room itself is deficient in bass response, the problem is aggravated. The second disadvantage of a small room is the wide spread among the resonances below 100 cps. Even if they are well distributed, there simply aren't enough of them to provide an audibly smooth response in the 50- to 100-cps region, where most materials have little absorption and can provide little useful damping.

Since larger rooms are desirable, but ceilings over 8 feet high are rarely practical in homes, the 1¼-ratio rule cannot be adhered to strictly. Two satisfactory compromises can be made.

It is possible to multiply the actual height dimension by two in order to serve as a basis for calculation of the width and length. This was done in designing Acoustic Research's audio demonstration room in the Better Living Building at the 1964-1965 New York World's Fair. The actual inside dimensions are 27.5 by 21.75 by 8.7 feet. The height is just half what it should be ideally. Standing-wave frequency distribution is quite respectable, although some gaps associated with the missing full height dimension are detectable.

As a second compromise, this procedure can be further modified by reducing the width slightly to compensate for the reduced height dimension. Such a room might have dimensions of 25 by 17.5 by 7.75 feet. Ideally they should have been 25 by 20 by 15.5 feet, but the height was cut in half and the ratio of length to width was changed to 1.4 to 1. A good distribution of resonances below 90 cps was obtained at the expense of some clustering just above and below 100 cps.

ACOUSTIC TREATMENT AND FURNISHINGS

If room surfaces and furnishings reflected sound energy perfectly, then any sound radiated into a room would continue to rebound and reverberate for a very long time—until it finally became dissipated as heat by the air itself. Fortunately, this doesn't happen in practical cases, because room surfaces and furnishings do in fact absorb some sound energy. When they do, there is a beneficial side effect: the room resonances become less acute. The standing-wave pressure maximums are reduced in intensity, and the nulls become merely locations of somewhat reduced pressure. In other words, the resonances are damped by absorption. As the absorption increases, each standing wave becomes less severe and its effect is spread over a wider frequency range; the sound pressure is spread more evenly throughout the room; the average pressure in the room, and therefore the average loudness, decreases; and the sound becomes more dead, less reverberant.

It should be evident that absorption (like many good things) can be carried to excess. Materials vary widely in absorption characteristics, however, and common materials used with common sense can be used to avert or to correct most undesirable acoustic conditions.

Room-resonance damping is controllable with moderate ease from, say, 100 cps upward. Normal construction materials, room furnishings, and wall and floor treatments will usually provide acceptable control. A room furnished in spartan contemporary manner, with few drapes, uncarpeted floors, and virtually no upholstered pieces cannot help but make music sound overly bright and hard. A room with wall-to-wall carpet, heavy drapes on much of the wall area, "acoustical" tile on the ceiling, and a lot of overstuffed furniture will make music sound as if every instrument were filled with cotton batting. In this matter the middle of the road is best.

Do not, for example, have two completely hard or two very absorptive walls opposite one another. If one wall is mostly wallpapered or painted plaster, the wall opposite should have a significant part of its area "soft"—well-draped windows, wall hangings, bookcases (with books) and so on. Avoid acoustic tile on the ceiling; ordinary plaster is fine if you intend to cover a large part of the floor with area rugs. If you insist on tiled floors with no rugs, use Hushkote plaster or moderately soft (but not acoustic) tile on the ceiling. A mixture of hard-surfaced and upholstered furniture should be used, with the upholstered pieces placed near the hard walls if possible.

Hard, rigid surfaces in general have low absorption, while soft, padded surfaces have relatively high absorption. Painted brick, ceramic tile, concrete, glass, wood flooring or polished solid wood, linoleum, and most floor tile all have low absorption at all frequencies. Unpainted brick has very low absorption at frequencies below 1,000 cps, but its absorption rises slightly at higher frequencies. Ordinary plaster and plasterboard have fairly low absorption at all frequencies.

Wood paneling of ⅜-inch thickness or less, with an air space (partition studding, for example) behind it is one of the few building materials that has high absorption at moderately low frequencies but low absorption at higher frequencies, and for that reason is often useful. Most materials behave in an opposite way; acoustic tile has extremely high absorption at 500 cps and higher, but its absorption decreases sharply below that frequency. This is a useful characteristic for noise reduction in offices and public areas, but gives an unnatural environment for music listening.

Rough-textured carpeting with underlining has absorption that is fairly low at 125 cps but rises gradually until it is quite high at 3,000 cps and above. Without underlining, the absorption is reduced by half. Soft drapes hung straight against the wall or covering a window are similar in effect to carpet without underlining. Lining the material with a double thickness makes it roughly equivalent to carpet with underlining. Hanging the drapes well away from the wall appreciably increases absorption at low frequencies.

Upholstered chairs and sofas have high absorption and, significantly, they remain quite effective down to low frequencies. Open windows and doorways can be considered completely absorptive (since they reflect no sound at all) down to frequencies at which their dimensions are equal to or less than one wave length. For doors and windows of typical size this occurs at around 350 cps.

People also are efficient sound absorbers. They are most efficient in this capacity at about 2,000 cps, at which frequency they are roughly the equivalent of small sofas; at 250 cps, however, they absorb no more than upholstered chairs.

Most materials have relatively low absorption below 100 cps. Accordingly, it is difficult to damp severe resonances in this frequency region. The most satisfactory answer, of course, is to avoid them by choosing proper dimensions for the room. If that isn't possible—or if the room is already built and you are stuck with it—it is often possible to build a false partition or a partial room divider to break up the worst resonance. Finally, you can place the speaker systems in locations where they simply will not stimulate an offending standing wave.

Standing-wave nulls may be formed at any location in the room except at the eight three-surface junctions where two walls come together with the floor or ceiling. If a speaker system is located at a minimum-pressure point for any particular standing wave, it cannot generate that frequency efficiently. It is necessary only to locate suitable minimum-pressure points for that frequency along a convenient wall and put the speaker systems there. These points can be found either by calculation (if the frequency and the room dimensions are known), or by using your ears as a detector.

Room walls themselves are not perfectly stiff. If they are too flexible they will flex when the room is excited at very low frequencies, and it will not be possible to build up good low-frequency response in the room.

This is damping in a sense, but it is damping where it is not often needed. The objectionable resonances usually occur at frequencies above those at which wall, ceiling, or floor flexure is significant, with the result that the flexing can do harm but no compensating good.

Walls and ceilings can be made more stiff than is usual in common home construction, at relatively little expense, by specifying three or four coats of plaster instead of the usual two. Still more stiffness can be obtained by decreasing the normal spacing between floor and ceiling joists, and of wall studs; and by applying a layer of plywood to the joists or studs under the plaster lath. Walls constructed of brick, needless to say, are extremely rigid.

In concert halls, which are always large compared to typical home listening rooms, it is desirable that sound should reverberate for a relatively long time. This is not true of a room intended for listening to reproduced music—even a relatively large room. Large rooms require *more* absorptive treatment in proportion to size than do small rooms in order to obtain satisfactory damping of resonances.

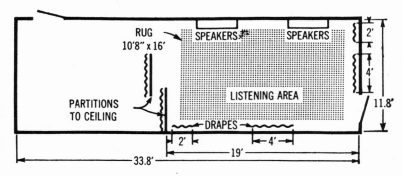

Floor plan of AR's demonstration room in Grand Central Station. Here an existing structure was modified for the suppression of certain resonances and the creation of others.

What can be done to amend the acoustic properties of an existing room? An excellent example is supplied by AR's Music Room on the west balcony of Grand Central Station in New York City. The structure as acquired was very long and narrow and proved to be impossible for audio demonstrations. The room shape was changed by adding solid ¾-inch wood semi-partitions, heavily braced with 2 x 4 studs, from floor to ceiling. Cork sheeting (with its peculiar absorption properties) was removed from the walls, which were then braced with closely-spaced 2 x 4 studs. Plywood and plasterboard were applied over the wall studding; this restored the missing low bass tones.

Other measures taken included plastering over an acoustic-tile ceiling, and replacement of the wall-to-wall carpeting with a rug which left some of the marble floor exposed. Drapes were hung on a trial-and-error basis until the best sound was obtained.

The modifications yielded a listening area of 19 by 11.8 feet, with a ceiling height of 9.3 feet. Note that the ceiling height is almost exactly half the room length, a coincidence that could have been troublesome. For all standing waves associated with the fundamental height resonance there is a null at half the room height, and the speakers are located on wall opposite the listening area at just about that height. Consequently these resonances are excited by the speakers to only a small degree; some potentially unpleasant resonant-frequency bunching is thereby avoided. (Even so, it was still found to be impossible to face the speakers into the long dimension of the room.)

All these changes together transformed a room with intolerable acoustic properties into one that is now generally conceded to be excellent. Comparable modifications were applied successfully also to the AR Music Room on Brattle Street in Cambridge, Massachusetts.

7.

MAKING SYSTEM ADJUSTMENTS

W HEN YOU have your new stereo system installed and wired up the first
thing you'll do, probably, is to put on some music and listen to it. We'd do
the same thing ourselves. After you've listened for a while (next day, perhaps) you may be more willing to undertake the few adjustments that are
necessary to extract the best possible sound from your components.

PHASING THE SPEAKERS

The first thing you must do is to get your speakers into phase. To do this,
set all controls to their normal positions. All tweeter level controls on your
speaker systems should be set to the indicated normal settings. Put all bass
and treble controls in their normal or flat positions, rumble and scratch
filters in their "Flat" or "Out" positions, and loudness compensation
switches off. (The last-named switch may be labelled "Loudness-Volume"
— put it on "Volume.")

Now switch the stereo function selector to one of its monaural positions (or the blend control for maximum blend), the input selector switch
or switches to a phono position, the balance control (if one is provided)
to normal or central position, and the main volume control or controls
down. Turn on the system and put on a record. Turn up volume controls
and adjust the balance control, if necessary, until you get equal sound
levels from the speaker systems.

With the controls set this way you will have identical signals in both
channels of your stereo system (precise balance between the two channels
isn't necessary at this point). If the speaker systems are in phase the diaphragms will be moving in and out simultaneously; if they are out of
phase, the diaphragms of one system will be moving inward while those
of the other move outward.

There are two ways you can check the phasing easily. First, move the speaker systems together, side by side. Disconnect the speaker wires from one power amplifier. Listen to the sound from the speaker system still operating and concentrate on the solidity of the deep bass tones. Touch the disconnected speaker wires momentarily to the amplifier terminals from which you just removed them, noting the change in deep bass sound level, and then reverse the wires to the terminals. One way should produce increased bass level and the other way decreased bass level. The speaker systems are in phase with that connection which increased the bass level. Do not make any other changes, but mark these cable connections at the terminals of both amplifiers and speaker systems.

You can and should verify your results with the other common method for determining phasing. Move the speakers apart to their normal locations. With the speakers being fed identical signals as outlined above, try reversing the speaker wire connections at one power amplifier's output terminals. If you stand exactly midway between the speakers and in front of them by about the distance they are separated, the in-phase connection will give you the impression of a unified small sound source about halfway between the speaker systems. The out-of-phase connection should give you the impression of a disembodied sound which is difficult to locate precisely as you move your head about.

To ascertain that the pickup cartridge phasing is correct, repeat the test with the function selector switch in a stereo position, the blend control, if any, set for minimum blending, and a monaural record on the turntable. (If you have a stereo power amplifier with a stereo-mono switch, put the switch in the stereo position.) If you do not get the same results with the same speaker cable connections, then either you have made incorrect connections at the pickup cartridge output terminals or at the terminal board beneath the turntable. Recheck the pickup arm and cartridge wiring in that event.

Once the correct phasing is established, and you have marked the speaker and amplifier terminals and the speaker cables, you won't have to be concerned about this point again unless you replace one of the components.

ADJUSTING TWEETER CONTROLS

Now you are ready to adjust tweeter level controls on your speaker systems for proper balance among the frequency ranges covered by the individual speakers within each system. The basic procedure is the same for either two-way (one tweeter level control) or three-way (one mid-range and one tweeter level control) speaker systems. It is a simple procedure but one which has several steps.

Setting tweeter controls should be done with your record player as a signal source. Monaural records should be used. If your main source of stereo will be records, the system should be switched into a stereo mode; if most of your serious stereo listening will be done with tape or broadcast sources, the system should be in the A + B monaural mode or the blend control should be set for maximum blending of the two channels. (If your system has no provision for combining both input channels and feeding the combination to both output channels, use whatever monaural mode is available on the function selector switch.) Use monaural records.

Set all filters out of the circuit, and all bass and treble tone controls in the indicated flat positions. The master volume control(s) should be set as you would normally have them for serious listening.

Because room position will affect audible balance, the loudspeaker systems should be set up where they will be normally used. Disconnect one lead to your center-channel speaker if you have one.

Begin with all level controls on the backs of the speaker systems turned all the way down. For AR-1, AR-2^x, AR-2a^x, AR-3, and AR-4 systems, this will leave only the woofer of each system operating. If you have AR-2 or AR-2a systems, temporarily remove the straps between terminals 2 and T. Again, this will leave only the woofer of each system operating.

With your system playing a monaural record and set up as described in the preceding paragraphs, adjust the preamp's balance control (or readjust slightly the two sections of your concentric master volume control) until you have the sound exactly centered between the speaker systems. *Do not* readjust these controls during the rest of this procedure.

Now disconnect temporarily *one* lead from the input terminals of the right-channel speaker system, leaving only the left-channel woofer operating. Reconnect the strap between terminals 2 and T of the left-channel speaker system (if you have had to disconnect it) and turn up the tweeter level control (AR-1, AR-2, AR-2^x, or AR-4) or the mid-range control (AR-2a, AR-2a^x, or AR-3) until you obtain what seems to be the most natural, life-like sound.

Listen to the system this way for some time, trying different monaural records until you are satisfied that the tonal balance is right. Then mark and leave the control at that setting. Leave the super-tweeter control of an AR-2a, AR-2a^x, or AR-3 turned down.

Reconnect the lead you had removed from one input terminal of the right-hand speaker system and, if it is an AR-2 or AR-2a, replace the strap between terminals 2 and T. Still playing a monaural record, and with the preamp settings unchanged, turn up the right-channel tweeter level control or the mid-range control (AR-2a, AR-2a^x, or AR-3) until, as in the phasing tests, the entire sound is centered exactly between the two speaker systems when you stand midway in front of them. This control should be adjusted so that centering is obtained for sounds of all pitches, including sibilants.

The two speaker systems now, if played alternately, should sound very much alike.

Finally, the super-tweeter level controls should be set properly so as to maintain this balance. If you have AR-2a, AR-2a^x, or AR-3 systems, disconnect the lead from one input terminal of the right-channel speaker system, leaving once again only the left-channel speaker system playing. Turn up the left-channel super-tweeter level control carefully until you can hear it begin to affect the total sound. Its effect should be subtle; if you can hear it make a *distinct* contribution of its own, turn it down a bit. Then leave it set there, and mark the setting.

Reconnect the input lead to the right-channel speaker system, and turn up its super-tweeter level control until, once more, the sound is centered between the systems. In making this final adjustment pay particular attention to sibilants, triangles, drum brush strokes, and similar "rustling" kinds of sounds. The record must be of extremely wide range and good quality. Again, you should find that the two systems sound alike if played alternately.

Perhaps the most satisfactory way to set the tweeter level controls on a center-channel speaker system, if you have one, is to note the settings of corresponding controls on the side-channel systems, and set the center-channel controls to approximately the same positions.

After setting the tweeter level controls for the most natural sound in your listening room, probably you will find that they are not exactly on the indicated normal settings. This should cause no concern.

SETTING VOLUME CONTROLS

There are so many possible combinations of volume, loudness, and input level controls, and variations in location of each, that it would be excessively complicated to give a general discussion which would take all into account at once. The italic introductions to the following sections should be scanned and only those which apply need be read. The necessary adjustments should be made in the order described.

Power Amplifier Input Level Controls. Power amplifiers may or may not have input level controls. If yours do, and if the amplifiers are identical in manufacture and model (or if it is a dual stereo amplifier) turn the controls all the way up and leave them there. No further adjustment is required.

If the amplifiers are not identical, turn both of the controls all the way up temporarily. Turn the master volume control (or controls, if there are separate concentric ones for each channel) on the preamp or stereo adapter all the way down. Turn all other preamp volume, input level, and separate loudness controls all the way up. Put the function selector in stereo position, the input selector(s) in the phono position, and the balance control, if any, in the central (normal) position. Tone controls should be set at normal too.

Start playing a monaural record. Then turn up the master volume control (if there are concentric controls for the two channels, turn them up by the same amount) until you obtain a comfortable sound level. Note which speaker system is the louder one. Now turn down the input level control on the power amplifier driving that speaker system until the sound levels from the two are equal or until, from a position in the center of the general listening area, the sound seems centered between the speaker systems.

Monaural Preamps with Stereo Adapter. These differ from single-chassis stereo preamps, and integral stereo preamp-amplifier combinations, in that they have an extra set of front-panel volume and/or loudness controls.

The volume/loudness controls on the adapter are combined for the two channels, either by a common control shaft or by a concentric clutch-type mechanism, and should be used as the master control(s). Those on the monaural preamp front panels should not be used as operating controls.

The manufacturer of the adapter may have suggested setting the monaural preamp front-panel volume and/or loudness controls all the way up.

His recommendation should be followed. If he has made no suggestion on this matter, see Appendix B (p. 89).

Preamp Input Level Controls. If you have input level-set controls on the preamp back panel(s), please refer to Appendix B (p. 89) for information on their adjustment.

Signal Source Output Settings. To establish the proper output volume control settings for signal sources, *when there are no preamp input level controls,* use the following procedure:

First, turn the preamp's function selector to a monaural mode, the input selector(s) to phono, the balance control (if there is any) to its normal or central setting, and other controls to their normal or flat positions.

Second, put on a record and set the master volume control(s) for a comfortable listening level.

Third, without changing the master volume control position, switch the input selector(s) to the other signal sources and adjust their output volume controls to give approximately the same sound levels as the record. For a stereo source it will be necessary to switch the function selector to the stereo mode, and adjust the relative settings of the source's output volume controls so as to obtain proper stereo balance between the speaker systems.

Mark the settings of the signal source output volume controls, so that you can return to them easily.

CENTER-CHANNEL SPEAKERS

If you have a center-channel speaker, don't try to drive it from the two side-channel power amplifiers directly; it should be driven by a separate power amplifier which is fed a sum signal derived from the two side channels. Some stereo preamps have a sum-signal output jack for connection to a center-channel amplifier. If yours does not, you can obtain an appropriate signal with a small microphone mixer (such as Switchcraft Model 310), connected as shown in the accompanying diagram.

The level control for the center-channel output on a preamp should be turned up until the contribution of the center speaker to the total sound becomes just faintly audible, and then turned back very slightly. If you use an external mixer, both controls on the mixer should be turned up by the same amount to achieve a similar effect.

A center-channel speaker should be phased with the other two after you have adjusted its level. Do not disturb the already-phased connections to the two side-channel amplifiers and speakers; the center-channel speaker must be phased to correspond with them. If the center-channel speaker system is a full-range one, either of the phasing procedures described previously will work. If you are using a speaker system which operates only in the upper frequency ranges, on the other hand, the second phasing method must be used.

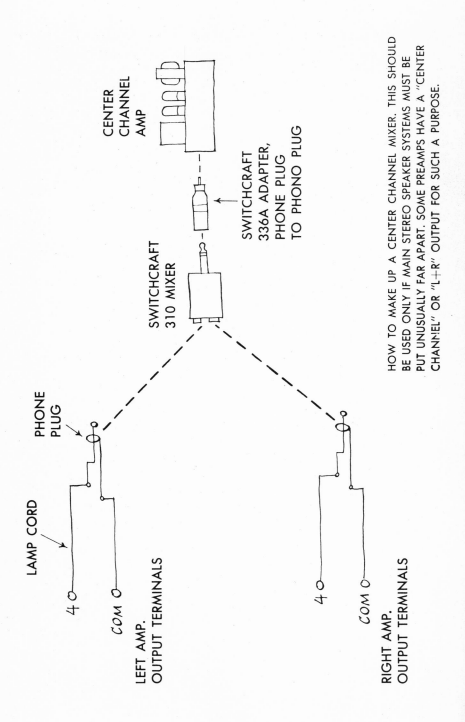

CENTER
CHANNEL
AMP

SWITCHCRAFT
336A ADAPTER,
PHONE PLUG
TO PHONO PLUG

SWITCHCRAFT
310 MIXER

PHONE
PLUG

LAMP CORD

4

COM

LEFT AMP.
OUTPUT TERMINALS

4

COM

RIGHT AMP.
OUTPUT TERMINALS

HOW TO MAKE UP A CENTER CHANNEL MIXER. THIS SHOULD
BE USED ONLY IF MAIN STEREO SPEAKER SYSTEMS MUST BE
PUT UNUSUALLY FAR APART. SOME PREAMPS HAVE A "CENTER
CHANNEL" OR "L+R" OUTPUT FOR SUCH A PURPOSE.

HUM BALANCING

Adjustment of hum balance controls, when they are provided, should be done with the system set up to play stereo records. The turntable motor should be switched on but the pickup arm should be left at rest position. Advance the master volume control to a little higher than normal setting; then turn up the bass tone control fully for the left channel only. Advance the master volume control still more, if necessary, to make the hum clearly audible. Then carefully adjust the left-channel hum balance control for minimum hum. Turn down the left-channel bass tone control and turn up the right-channel bass tone control, and adjust the right-channel hum balance control for minimum hum. Restore the operating controls to normal positions before playing a record.

8.

IN CASE OF DIFFICULTY

U SUALLY, with a reasonable application of common sense, problems in stereo systems can be tracked down by the user and cured. Even if you aren't skilled enough to cure an ailing amplifier all by yourself, you can obviously assure yourself of more expeditious servicing if you at least know that it *is* your amplifier that is at fault, rather than your speaker or some other component.

It is the experience of most manufacturers that a great deal of time is wasted by customers who blame the wrong component when their hi-fi system goes out of commission. The troubleshooting charts on the follow-ing pages are, therefore, designed to permit you to isolate the defective component that may be causing your stereo system to operate improperly —or not at all. Based on simple logic and on probabilities, the charts are not, of course, infallible—but fortunately they will work *most of the time.*

Stereo systems are actually easier to troubleshoot than monaural ones because usually only one channel will go bad. In such a case, a little switching of wiring connections will permit you to "exchange" one channel for another within a particular unit, thus quickly pinning down the com-ponent (or interconnecting cables) responsible for your problem.

This simple substitution process can also be extended to complete units when both channels have gone bad: just borrow an amplifier or other unit from a friend and substitute it temporarily for your own. If the trouble disappears when (for example) you put his amplifier in place of yours, then it is obviously your amplifier, and not some other component, that is the cause of malfunction.

58

A note of explanation: when the charts refer to a "source," they mean a primary signal source such as a record player, tuner, or tape machine. These sources are all presumed to be in stereo. In using the charts on the pages that follow, begin *in every case* with Chart I, labeled "Poor Sound or No Sound." You will be directed to other charts if required.

CHART I
POOR SOUND OR NO SOUND
FIRST STEPS

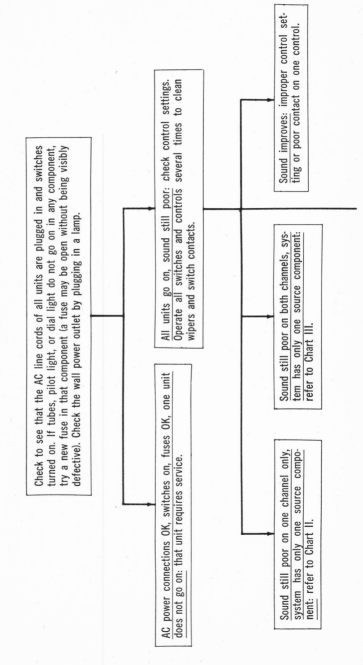

Check to see that the AC line cords of all units are plugged in and switches turned on. If tubes, pilot light, or dial light do not go on in any component, try a new fuse in that component (a fuse may be open without being visibly defective). Check the wall power outlet by plugging in a lamp.

AC power connections OK, switches on, fuses OK, one unit does not go on: that unit requires service.

All units go on, sound still poor: check control settings. Operate all switches and controls several times to clean wipers and switch contacts.

Sound still poor on one channel only, system has only one source component: refer to Chart II.

Sound still poor on both channels, system has only one source component: refer to Chart III.

Sound improves: improper control setting or poor contact on one control.

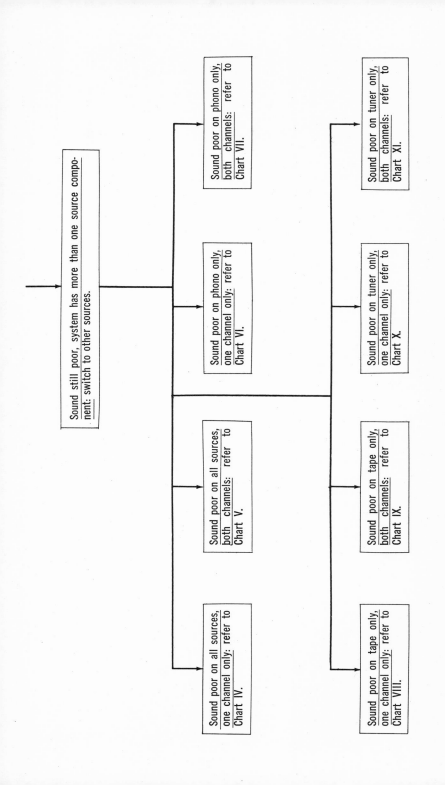

CHART II
SYSTEM HAS ONE SOURCE COMPONENT ONLY
SOUND POOR ON ONE CHANNEL

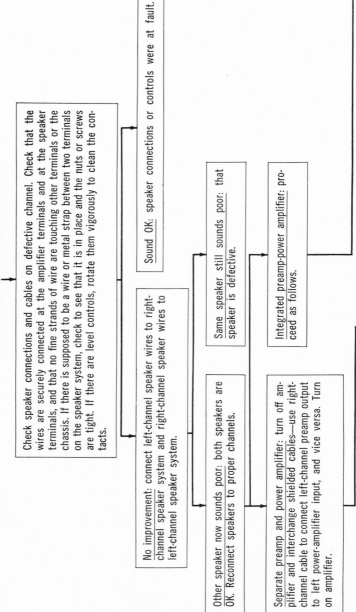

Check speaker connections and cables on defective channel. Check that the wires are securely connected at the amplifier terminals and at the speaker terminals, and that no fine strands of wire are touching other terminals or the chassis. If there is supposed to be a wire or metal strap between two terminals on the speaker system, check to see that it is in place and the nuts or screws are tight. If there are level controls, rotate them vigorously to clean the contacts.

Sound OK: speaker connections or controls were at fault.

No improvement: connect left-channel speaker wires to right-channel speaker system and right-channel speaker wires to left-channel speaker system.

Same speaker still sounds poor: that speaker is defective.

Integrated preamp-power amplifier: proceed as follows.

Other speaker now sounds poor: both speakers are OK. Reconnect speakers to proper channels.

Separate preamp and power amplifier: turn off amplifier and interchange shielded cables—use right-channel cable to connect left-channel preamp output to left power-amplifier input, and vice versa. Turn on amplifier.

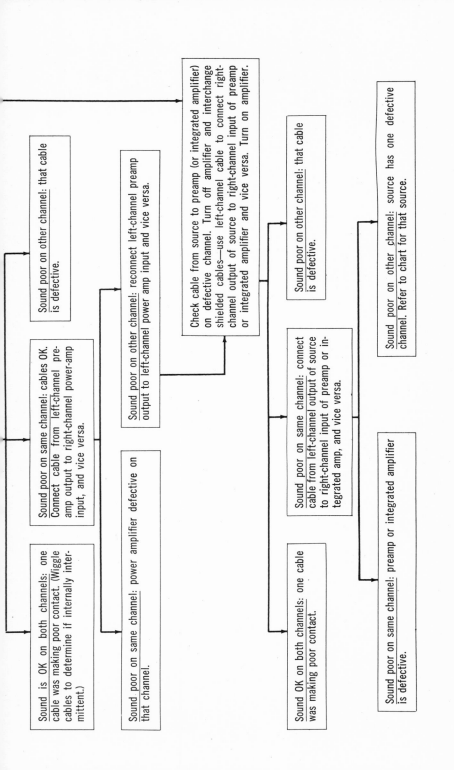

CHART III

SYSTEM HAS ONE SOURCE COMPONENT ONLY
SOUND POOR ON BOTH CHANNELS

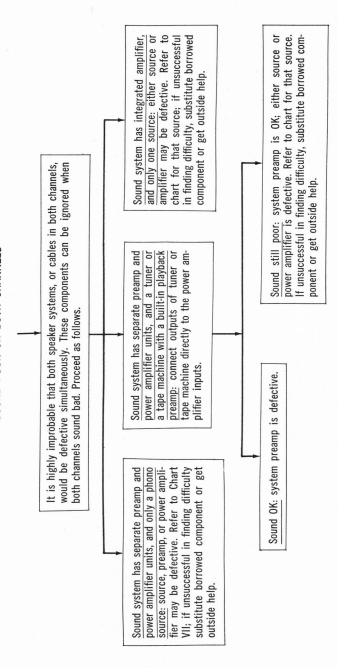

It is highly improbable that both speaker systems, or cables in both channels, would be defective simultaneously. These components can be ignored when both channels sound bad. Proceed as follows.

Sound system has separate preamp and power amplifier units, and only a phono source: source, preamp, or power amplifier may be defective. Refer to Chart VII; if unsuccessful in finding difficulty substitute borrowed component or get outside help.

Sound system has separate preamp and power amplifier units, and a tuner or a tape machine with a built-in playback preamp: connect outputs of tuner or tape machine directly to the power amplifier inputs.

Sound system has integrated amplifier, and only one source: either source or amplifier may be defective. Refer to chart for that source; if unsuccessful in finding difficulty, substitute borrowed component or get outside help.

Sound OK: system preamp is defective.

Sound still poor: system preamp is OK; either source or power amplifier is defective. Refer to chart for that source. If unsuccessful in finding difficulty, substitute borrowed component or get outside help.

CHART V

SOUND POOR ON MORE THAN ONE SOURCE,
BOTH CHANNELS

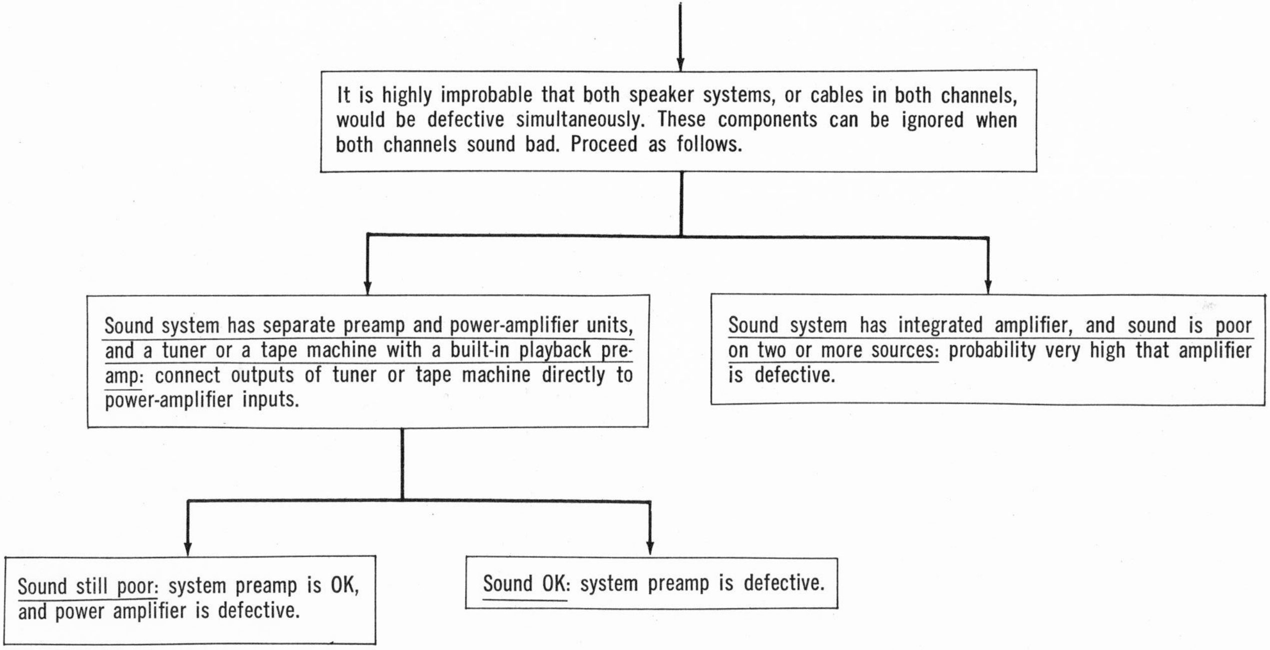

It is highly improbable that both speaker systems, or cables in both channels, would be defective simultaneously. These components can be ignored when both channels sound bad. Proceed as follows.

Sound system has integrated amplifier, and sound is poor on two or more sources: probability very high that amplifier is defective.

Sound system has separate preamp and power-amplifier units, and a tuner or a tape machine with a built-in playback pre-amp: connect outputs of tuner or tape machine directly to power-amplifier inputs.

Sound OK: system preamp is defective.

Sound still poor: system preamp is OK, and power amplifier is defective.

CHART IV

SOUND POOR ON MORE THAN ONE SOURCE,
ONE CHANNEL ONLY

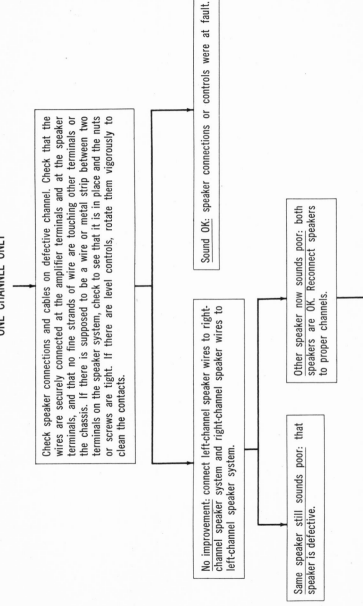

Check speaker connections and cables on defective channel. Check that the wires are securely connected at the amplifier terminals and at the speaker terminals, and that no fine strands of wire are touching other terminals or the chassis. If there is supposed to be a wire or metal strip between two terminals on the speaker system, check to see that it is in place and the nuts or screws are tight. If there are level controls, rotate them vigorously to clean the contacts.

Sound OK: speaker connections or controls were at fault.

No improvement: connect left-channel speaker wires to right-channel speaker system and right-channel speaker wires to left-channel speaker system.

Same speaker still sounds poor: that speaker is defective.

Other speaker now sounds poor: both speakers are OK. Reconnect speakers to proper channels.

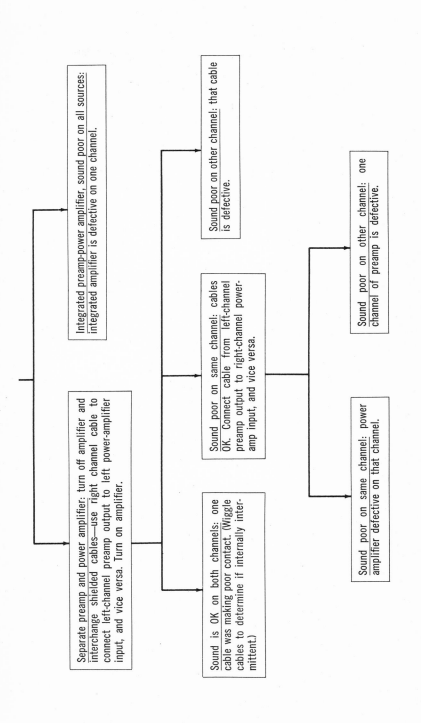

Separate preamp and power amplifier: turn off amplifier and interchange shielded cables—use right channel cable to connect left-channel preamp output to left power-amplifier input, and vice versa. Turn on amplifier.

Integrated preamp-power amplifier, sound poor on all sources: integrated amplifier is defective on one channel.

Sound poor on other channel: that cable is defective.

Sound is OK on both channels: one cable was making poor contact. (Wiggle cables to determine if internally intermittent.)

Sound poor on same channel: cables OK. Connect cable from left-channel preamp output to right-channel power-amp input, and vice versa.

Sound poor on other channel: one channel of preamp is defective.

Sound poor on same channel: power amplifier defective on that channel.

CHART VI

SOUND POOR ON PHONO ONLY (OTHER SOURCE OK), ONE CHANNEL ONLY

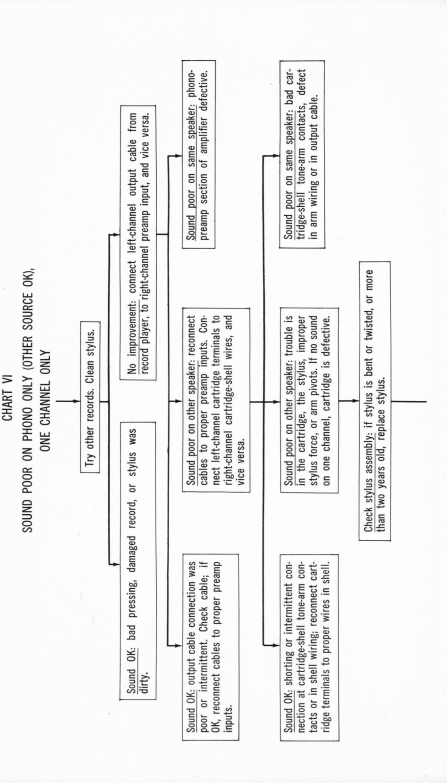

Try other records. Clean stylus.

Sound OK: bad pressing, damaged record, or stylus was dirty.

No improvement: connect left-channel output cable from record player, to right-channel preamp input, and vice versa.

Sound poor on same speaker: phono-preamp section of amplifier defective.

Sound OK: output cable connection was poor or intermittent. Check cable; if OK, reconnect cables to proper preamp inputs.

Sound poor on other speaker: reconnect cables to proper preamp inputs. Connect left-channel cartridge terminals to right-channel cartridge-shell wires, and vice versa.

Sound poor on same speaker: bad cartridge-shell tone-arm contacts, defect in arm wiring or in output cable.

Sound OK: shorting or intermittent connection at cartridge-shell tone-arm contacts or in shell wiring; reconnect cartridge terminals to proper wires in shell.

Sound poor on other speaker: trouble is in the cartridge, the stylus, improper stylus force, or arm pivots. If no sound on one channel, cartridge is defective.

Check stylus assembly: if stylus is bent or twisted, or more than two years old, replace stylus.

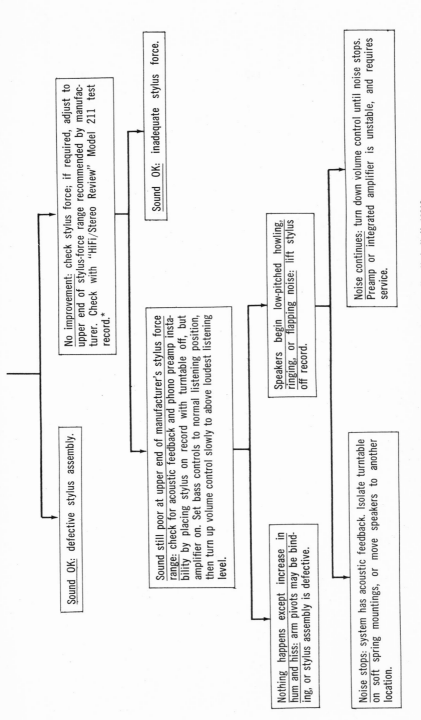

*Available at $4.95 from "HiFi/Stereo Review," 1 Park Avenue, New York, N. Y. 10016.

CHART VII

SOUND POOR ON PHONO ONLY (OTHER SOURCES OK), BOTH CHANNELS

Try other records. Clean stylus.

Sound OK: bad pressing, damaged record, or stylus was dirty.

No improvement: check speed setting.

Sound OK: wrong speed setting.

Speed setting OK: check for flutter and rumble, using "HiFi/Stereo Review" Model 211 test record.*

High rumble or flutter: clean belts and pulleys; lubricate bearing according to manufacturer's instructions.

Flutter and rumble OK: check stylus assembly. If stylus shank is bent or twisted, or more than two years old, replace stylus.

Sound OK: stylus was defective.

No improvement: check stylus force. If required, adjust to upper end of stylus-force range recommended by manufacturer. Check with Model 211 test record.*

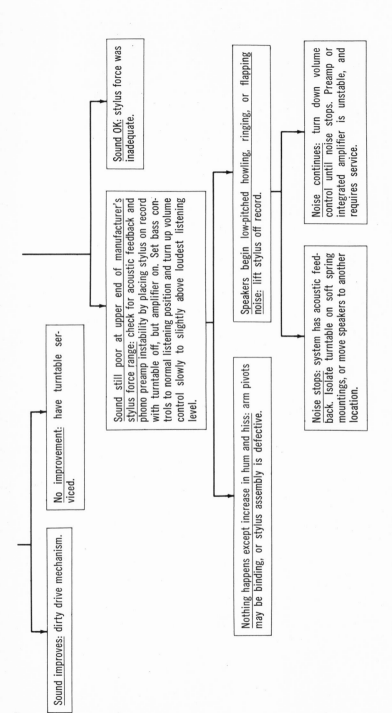

Sound improves: dirty drive mechanism.

No improvement: have turntable serviced.

Sound OK: stylus force was inadequate.

Sound still poor at upper end of manufacturer's stylus force range: check for acoustic feedback and phono preamp instability by placing stylus on record with turntable off, but amplifier on. Set bass controls to normal listening position and turn up volume control slowly to slightly above loudest listening level.

Nothing happens except increase in hum and hiss: arm pivots may be binding, or stylus assembly is defective.

Speakers begin low-pitched howling, ringing, or flapping noise: lift stylus off record.

Noise stops: system has acoustic feedback. Isolate turntable on soft spring mountings, or move speakers to another location.

Noise continues: turn down volume control until noise stops. Preamp or integrated amplifier is unstable, and requires service.

*Available at $4.95 from "HiFi/Stereo Review," 1 Park Avenue, New York, N. Y. 10016.

CHART VIII

SOUND POOR ON TAPE ONLY (OTHER SOURCES OK),
ONE CHANNEL ONLY

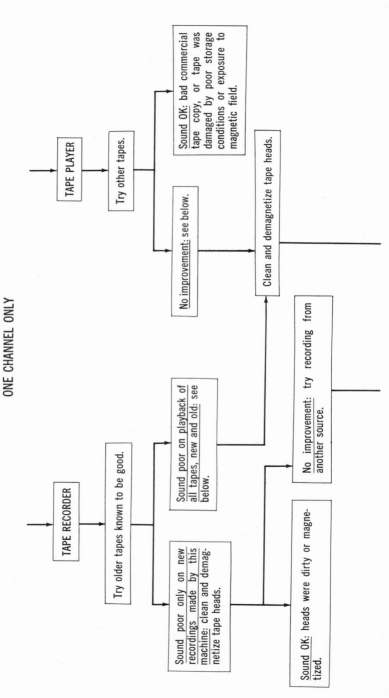

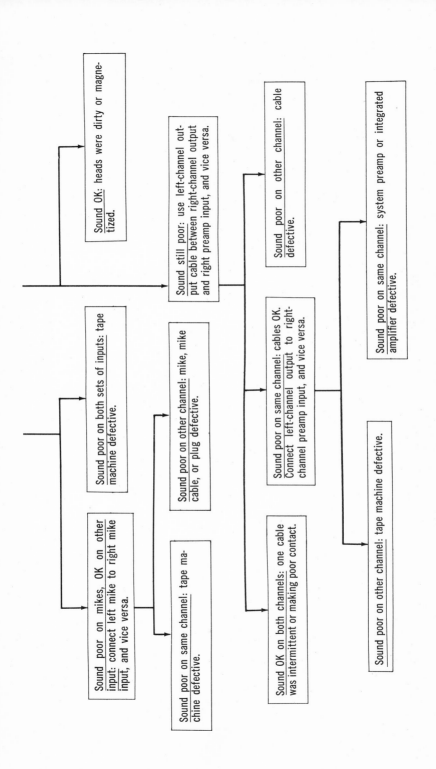

CHART IX

SOUND POOR ON TAPE ONLY (OTHER SOURCES OK), BOTH CHANNELS

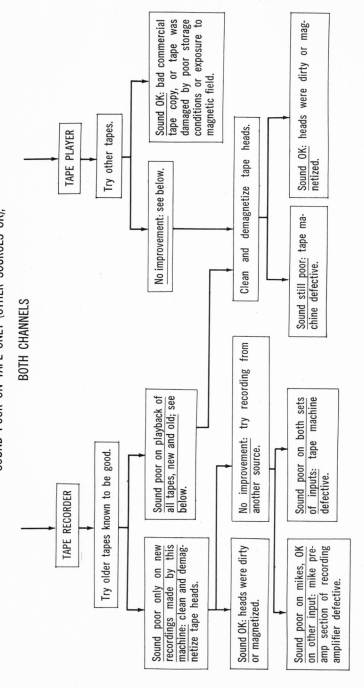

CHART X

SOUND POOR ON TUNER ONLY (OTHER SOURCES OK), ONE CHANNEL ONLY

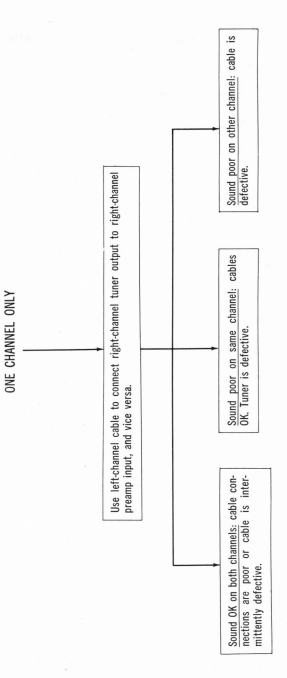

Use left-channel cable to connect right-channel tuner output to right-channel preamp input, and vice versa.

Sound OK on both channels: cable connections are poor or cable is intermittently defective.

Sound poor on same channel: cables OK. Tuner is defective.

Sound poor on other channel: cable is defective.

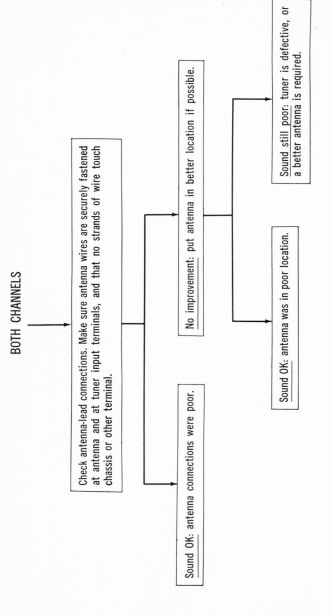

CHART XI

SOUND POOR ON TUNER ONLY (OTHER SOURCES OK),

BOTH CHANNELS

Check antenna-lead connections. Make sure antenna wires are securely fastened at antenna and at tuner input terminals, and that no strands of wire touch chassis or other terminal.

Sound OK: antenna connections were poor.

No improvement: put antenna in better location if possible.

Sound OK: antenna was in poor location.

Sound still poor: tuner is defective, or a better antenna is required.

HUM ELIMINATION

Excessive hum is a symptom that can have many causes. You can hear hum on just about any system if you turn up the volume controls to maximum, and turn up the bass tone controls too. These are hardly typical listening conditions, however. Hum should not be noticeable with the tone controls at normal position and the volume controls set for a fairly high (but not unreasonable) listening level. If you have hum under these conditions it is worth looking into.

If the hum increases when you touch the pickup arm, the arm is not grounded properly; if it increases when the turntable motor is switched on, the motor ground may not be connected properly. If you can't find the trouble, disconnect the existing ground wires to the arm itself (the fifth wire coming out of the arm, or the shield braid around the four cartridge wires—not the cartridge wires) and disconnect also the wire to the turntable motor. Then run separate insulated wires from the motor frame and the arm base to the preamp, soldering these wires to the outer shell of the RCA plug on the left-channel phono cable. If that doesn't help, you may have a defective cartridge or a faulty tube or circuit part in the phono section of the preamp.

Hum may be caused by loose-fitting or partially-inserted RCA plugs anywhere in the system. Check to see that the shells of all these plugs make good contact with the outer surface of the corresponding receptacles. Also, try flexing the connecting cables near the plugs. If the hum disappears momentarily it may indicate a defective cable.

If you are using monaural preamps with a stereo adapter, it is occasionally helpful to connect the two preamp chassis together with a heavy wire. This wire can be soldered to the shells of RCA plugs which are inserted into unused input jacks on each preamp. In some installations of this kind, on the other hand, hum may be reduced by partially withdrawing the RCA plug on *one* cable from a stereo tuner or tape player, so that the outer shell

does not make contact with the preamp input jack, but the inside pin still does make contact.

If the monaural preamps receive operating power from associated power amplifiers, try (one at a time) partially withdrawing the signal cable plugs at the power amplifier input jacks.

In all of these tests, turn off the AC power to the power amplifiers while changing cable connections.

Another trick, which doesn't help very often, is reversing the AC plug of the component which produces the hum, and if that doesn't work, reversing the AC plug of the preamp. It's worth a try. Also helpful occasionally is a heavy wire connection from the preamp chassis to a cold-water pipe, heating system radiator, or waste pipe.

Once you have isolated the hum to a particular electronic component (preamp, power amplifier, tuner, or tape machine), and have eliminated interconnecting cables as a cause, the next step is up to you—depending on your inclination toward doing-it-yourself. You have a fairly even chance of curing the trouble by replacing the tubes, one at a time, with spare ones of the same type. If replacing a tube doesn't help, remove the replacement and reinsert the old one. And after you've tried replacing all the tubes to no avail, outside help is indicated.

One final note on hum: don't overlook the possibility that it may be mechanical noise. The power transformer of an amplifier can buzz at a hum frequency if the mounting bolts or the windings aren't tight. Cures include tightening the mounting bolts and shock-mounting the amplifier on a soft pad. Leave holes for ventilation, of course.

LOW-FREQUENCY DISTURBANCES, DISTORTION

Excessive turntable rumble, heavy, muddy bass, or a flapping sound from one or both speakers, should these symptoms occur only when playing records, may be caused by acoustic feedback. If low-frequency vibrations from the speakers are able to get back to the record player and shake the pickup arm, the cartridge output is increased. This, when amplified, produces still more output from the speakers, and that shakes the arm even more. The result is either a peak in the system bass response or, at worst, a continuous low-frequency oscillation analogous to a howling PA system.

Acoustic feedback usually can be cured (or at least reduced to insignificance) by improving the shock mounts under the turntable. Putting the speakers on thick pads of foam rubber may help also, particularly if they rest on the floor. In some severe cases you may have no alternative to increasing the distance between the turntable and speakers.

Rumble (a heavy, grinding background noise when playing records) may be produced by the moving parts of the turntable. If you have such a noise after your system has been proved free of acoustic feedback, don't get upset immediately. Some new turntables require a few days to get broken in. Some records, too, have rumble from the cutting turntable which isn't audible except when they are played on systems having extended bass response. If the rumble persists and is evident on all records, try lubricating the turntable as the manufacturer recommends. You should take whatever steps are necessary to have the turntable replaced or repaired if it doesn't respond to lubrication.

Distortion, buzzing, shrieking, rattling, or rasping noises, or extreme mismatches in balance, may be caused by any component in the system—or by worn records. You may find that a good high-fidelity system will reveal only too clearly the damage done to your old records by the phonograph you have just discarded.

If the offending component is a record player, look closely at the stylus assembly to see if it has been bent or canted to one side accidentally; see that it has not collected a clump of dirt; recheck the stylus force; and make sure that the arm is perfectly free to move in all required directions. Because stereo needles are necessarily light and compliant, it is very easy to damage most types. It is good insurance to have a spare stylus assembly on hand.

WARRANTIES

When you find a defective component in a new system—that is, if the component is faulty upon installation—you have a right to expect the dealer to replace it immediately from stock.

If a component should develop a defect after it has been in use, but the warranty period has not expired, your dealer has an obligation to repair it promptly or to handle the details of shipping it to the manufacturer for repair.

After the warranty period has expired, the dealer may still feel a moral obligation to handle the repair for you, but you may not be able to make him do it if he doesn't feel so inclined. For that reason you should choose your dealer carefully.

Details of factory warranties vary, but certainly there should be no charge of any kind for replacement or prompt repair of any component found to be faulty when installed. You should expect to pay freight charges, at the most, for in-warranty repairs. (This assumes that the component has not been used abnormally or subjected to abuse.) A few manufacturers, including AR, Inc., refund prepaid freight expenses on repairs of defective components.

You should not hesitate to write directly to the manufacturer if you have no local dealer in whom you place your confidence. You should not return a component directly to the manufacturer without first getting written permission from him, however, and in your letter of complaint you should describe clearly the symptoms of the defect and the steps you have taken to ascertain that his component is actually the defective one. You should also ask him to send you a new shipping carton if you have not kept the old one with all the inner parts.

Upon receipt of the manufacturer's permission to return the defective unit, be sure to pack it correctly and carefully in the proper carton. Pack with the unit a slip of paper having your name and address and a description of the defect. Ship prepaid and, if you use parcel post, insured. Keep the insurance receipt until your component has been returned to you safely. Further damage during shipment is least likely if you use a highway freight trucking company for heavy items.

9.

OPERATION AND MAINTENANCE

Provided you take reasonably good care of your stereo system, and use it properly, it should give you many years of satisfaction. Routine preventive maintenance procedures are quite simple. Any fairly intelligent adult can handle them if he is interested in doing so; if you'd rather not be bothered, it is wise to find a competent high-fidelity service organization to do the job.

Every six months, each tube in the power amplifiers should be marked clearly as to its location, removed, and tested. Preamp tubes should be checked in the same way once per year. You can have them tested for a moderate fee at a reliable service shop. Substandard ones should be replaced, and the others should be put back into the same tube sockets from which they were taken.

Once a year, at least, record players and tape machines should have mechanical parts cleaned and lubricated according to directions in their instruction books. Every signal-cable plug in the system should be removed from its socket and reinserted, with a twisting motion, to get rid of any tarnish that may have formed.

Once every two years the pickup stylus assembly should be replaced whether or not the stylus shows wear. Stiffened stylus-damping material, or a slightly bent needle shank, can cause as much grief as a worn stylus; the cost of a new stylus is minor for the insurance it buys that you will have continuing good sound and minimal record wear. For the same reason, you should replace or have replaced once a year the idler wheels or belt of your turntable. Many have this work done during their annual vacation periods.

Once a month you should check and, if necessary, reset the pickup stylus force *if this is established by springs within the arm*. It isn't necessary to recheck stylus force so often if it is adjusted by means of a counterweight. If you have a tape machine the heads should be cleaned monthly with the recommended cleaning solution, and the heads demagnetized. These things are simple and don't require much time, but it is important that they be done regularly.

When some part of the system stops working completely or develops a defect suddenly, it is easy to notice it and take steps to correct it. A gradual deterioration from peak performance, on the other hand, may easily go unnoticed for a long time. It is almost impossible to remember accurately what a system used to sound like when it was new. These preventive maintenance routines, if followed faithfully, will minimize the possibility of such gradual deterioration.

EXTENDING RECORD LIFE

Depending entirely on how you treat them, your records may be ruined after two or three playings, or they may be almost like new after you've enjoyed them dozens of times.

Modern pickup cartridges press down on a record with a force that is only a small fraction of an ounce, it is true. Yet because the areas of contact between the needle and record groove walls are so exceedingly small, the pressure developed at these contact points may be thousands of pounds per square inch—enough to deform the record groove surface appreciably. In order to minimize the permanent effects of this deformation (and, accordingly, reduce record wear), your pickup cartridge and arm should be adjusted for the lowest stylus force *at which they will trace heavily-recorded passages well* without buzzes or fuzziness. We recommend that the stylus force be adjusted to the proper value by using the *HiFi/Stereo Review* Model 211 test record.*

Further, you should not play any part of a record repeatedly. Give the groove walls a chance to recover from this deformation before playing the record again. A day's rest should be enough.

Make it a habit to look at the needle occasionally, to see that it hasn't been bent by rough handling, and that it hasn't accumulated a ball of dust which might interfere with its motion. Bent needles must be replaced immediately; dirty ones should be cleaned by gently coaxing away the dirt with a very soft brush. The needle should be replaced after two years of use, even if it doesn't appear to need it, as explained in the preceding section.

As every record owner knows, records become warped easily. Severe warping, even if it does not make the record unplayable, accelerates record wear by increasing stylus force on the upward slope of the warp and decreasing it on the downward slope. You can keep warping under control by storing records on edge, in rows of only one record size; keeping moderate

* Available at $4.95 from *HiFi/Stereo Review,* 1 Park Avenue, New York, N. Y.

sidewise pressure on each row, between flat surfaces; keeping the records aligned in each row; and replacing records in the proper row immediately after playing them.

Perhaps the worst record problem, however, is dust and dirt. Records acquire static charges very easily as they are played. Even the act of removing a record from its jacket can generate a charge on it. When so charged, a record attracts dust particles from the air and from the turntable mat. These particles settle down in the grooves, whence they are impossible to remove with a cloth — even a damp cloth. When the needle encounters this dirt it makes those familiar crackling sounds in the loudspeaker and, at the same time, grinds up the dirt and roughens the groove walls permanently.

There are many liquids on the market which are supposed to prevent the build-up of static charges on records. Some are claimed to have "lubricating" properties also. Some, if used as directed, build up sludge deposits which do far more harm than good. There are two with which we have had good results; these are the liquid supplied with the Dust Bug, and with that applied by the Disc-Preener (provided it is applied lightly).

A Dust Bug record cleaner has its own spindle and tracks the record groove in synchronism with the tone arm.

In addition, it is necessary to remove dirt which settles in the groove even when the record has no significant static charge. This can be done with a brush having bristles shaped specifically for the job, such as the Dust Bug.

Very dirty records can best be cleaned by washing them carefully in a dilute solution of mild dishwashing detergent, rinsing thoroughly, and blotting them dry with a clean turkish towel.

Never touch the groove area with your fingers when handling records. Use only the outer edge and center area. With a little practice you'll find it easy to remove a record from its jacket, play it, and put it back without touching the groove area.

Records should be insulated from the outer jacket of heavy cardboard by an inner sleeve of hard, glossy paper, cellophane, or flexible plastic. If you lose or tear the inner sleeve it should be replaced; plastic sleeves for this purpose can be bought at record stores and high-fidelity component dealers.

CARING FOR TAPES

Under normal circumstances tapes do not suffer from contact with air-borne dust, and do not accumulate scratches. There are three possible sources of damage to recorded tapes that you should be on the lookout for, however.

First, partial erasure of the tape can occur if the tape machine heads are permitted to build up permanent magnetic charges. At least once a month the tape heads should be cleaned and demagnetized, as described in the tape machine maintenance section.

Second, partial erasure and odd distortion effects can occur if a reel of recorded tape is inadvertently put near a strong magnetic field from a loudspeaker, an "instant-heating" solder gun, an amplifier's power transformer, a large electric motor, a head demagnetizer, or similar device.

Third, excessive deviations from normal room temperature or humidity can make tape brittle, can curl the edges, or can make it stretch easily. Tape should not be stored in a cellar or attic, for example, or left inside a closed car in the sun. Remember that normal indoor living environments are required for storage over long periods; tape will be best off wherever you would be comfortable in light clothes.

OPERATIONAL PRECAUTIONS

You can help keep a high-fidelity system in good condition by operating it intelligently, too. For example, the performance of a fine speaker system is made possible only by taking advantage of the large ratio between peak and average power in music and speech program material. If you turn up the volume control high enough to overload a 60-watt power amplifier on orchestral peaks, the average power into the speaker system may be no more than three or four watts.

A tweeter voice coil must be wound of very fine wire if it is to be light enough to reproduce high frequencies well. Such a voice coil may be overheated and burned out by even moderate continuous power inputs, although it can be used safely in a speaker system which will handle music or speech inputs that overload a 100-watt amplifier on short-duration peaks.

It follows that speaker systems designed for home use should not be subjected to high-level frequency response testing, which represents a large continuous power input. By the same token, the rushing noise heard between FM stations should not be left applied at a high sound level for longer than a few seconds at a time. A defective power amplifier, oscillating at an ultrasonic frequency, can also burn out a tweeter quickly.

Similar precautions should be taken at the low end of the frequency scale. A severe case of acoustic feedback, or a badly rumbling turntable, is not likely to do any physical damage. It may, however, take up most of the available power-producing ability of an amplifier, or most of the power-handling ability of a woofer, so that the distortion of what you want to hear — the music — is very high. Turning up the bass tone controls unnaturally high, or incorrect use of a loudness control, can produce the same effect.

A fine phonograph pickup cartridge is necessarily quite delicate; it should be handled carefully with the respect it deserves. If it is knocked out of alignment it can't possibly work as it is supposed to.

High-fidelity systems are like other home appliances in one respect: if you misuse them or treat them shabbily, you will be disappointed in the results. Given reasonable care, however, they can reward you with thousands of hours of pleasure.

Good listening!

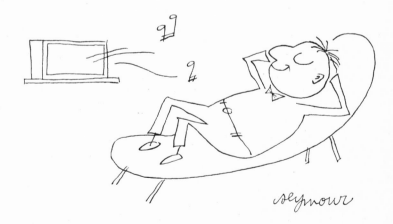

APPENDIX A

MOUNTING A TONE ARM

IF YOU have to install a tone arm on a turntable mounting board, be as accurate as you possibly can be in marking and drilling the arm holes. The most important dimension is the distance by which the stylus point over-hangs, or overreaches, the center of the turntable spindle.

Not many tone arm manufacturers specify this dimension, for which the optimal value varies according to the arm geometry. The distance from the turntable spindle to the center of the arm's horizontal pivot usually is given instead, and often a template for marking the arm pivot holes is supplied. This is helpful and is theoretically just as good a dimension pro-vided that the *pickup cartridge* mounting holes are the standard distance — ⅜ in. — in back of the stylus point. If this distance *is* standard (check to make sure), or if you are installing an integral arm/cartridge combination, you can feel safe in using the template or the spindle-to-arm-pivot dimen-sion specified. If not, the specified distance must be adjusted so as to com-pensate for the amount by which the cartridge mounting hole distance departs from the standard.

After the arm holes have been drilled in the turntable base, mount the arm *without* the stylus. Then adjust its height above the turntable accord-ing to the manufacturer's instructions.

Allow plenty of extra length in the leads from the arm before securing them below the base, so that they will not interfere even slightly with the movement of the arm. Check that the arm can move freely both hori-zontally and vertically; on some arms, for example, if the set screw for height adjustment is overtightened it makes the horizontal bearing sluggish.

MOUNTING CARTRIDGE IN SHELL

When you buy a pickup arm and cartridge separately, you will have to install the cartridge in the head shell. This shell is detachable from the end of just about every modern arm, which simplifies the assembly task.

Most shells have four wires, stripped at the ends, to which you must solder clips for the cartridge you intend to use. Clips of the proper size will be supplied with the cartridge. Be careful not to let solder run down into that part of the clip which slips over the cartridge contact pins, and don't hold the soldering tip on the joint any longer than necessary to make the solder flow on the wire and the end of the clip.

Instructions with the arm will tell you which wires are for left and right channels, and which are the "hot" wires for each channel. Instructions with the cartridge will identify the contact pins in a corresponding manner. Usually the clips must be put on the contact pins before installation of the cartridge in the shell.

The cartridge is held by two machine screws which go into tapped holes in the top of the shell. Remove the stylus assembly, or put the stylus shield in place, while installing the cartridge. Standoff bushings and screws of various length are furnished with the cartridge and arm; select those which permit the top of the cartridge to be as close to the top part of the shell as possible when the two are assembled. Tighten the two screws evenly and alternately so that the cartridge is not canted within the shell, and is aligned with it fore and aft.

When you have the cartridge tightened in place, tuck the wires up into the shell and check the clips to see that they are neither touching one another nor the contacts at the back part of the shell. If necessary, bend the ends of the clips gently to avoid the possibility of such shorts.

APPENDIX B

THIS SECTION need be read only if you have a stereo system with two monaural preamps and a stereo adapter.

SETTING CONTROLS FOR DUAL MONAURAL PREAMPS WITH STEREO ADAPTER

Setting Front-Panel Volume Controls. If the manufacturer of the stereo adapter does not advise setting the preamp front-panel volume controls all the way up, set them about ⅔ of the way up and switch the loudness compensation off. If the monaural preamps have separate continuously-variable loudness and volume controls, turn up the loudness controls all the way and turn up the volume controls about ⅔ of the way.

To check this adjustment for sound balance, turn down the adapter's master volume control(s). Turn any preamp *input* level controls all the way up, the function selector to Stereo, the balance control (if any) to its central or Normal position, and the selector switches to RIAA Phono. Other controls should be in the flat positions. Then put on a monaural record and turn up the adapter's master volume control(s) equally until the sound level is reasonable. Make fine adjustments in the monaural preamp volume controls to obtain equal (centered) sound from the two speaker systems. Mark the preamp volume control positions carefully and leave them set at those positions.

Preamp Input Level Controls. Although found in some stereo preamps too, input level controls are most likely to be encountered in monaural preamps used with stereo adapters. Before these controls can be adjusted properly, the front-panel volume/loudness controls on the monaural preamps must be set as described in the preceding paragraphs.

To set preamp input level controls, the function selector switch should be in a stereo position, the input selectors on Phono, and if there is a separate balance control it should be in the central (Normal) position. If there is a switch to apply loudness compensation to the master volume control(s), it should be in the ON position; if there is a separate master loudness control(s), it should be all the way up. The master volume control(s) should be turned all the way up. All preamp input level controls must be turned all the way down. Other controls should be in the flat positions.

Put on a monaural record (loud orchestral, preferably) and turn up both phono input level controls until the sound is just slightly louder than you'll ever want to listen to it seriously, while it remains centered between the speaker systems. Centering is obtained by relative adjustment of the two phono input level controls. Then turn down the master volume control(s) to a reasonable level before the neighbors descend on you. Leave the other controls as they are, however, and do not disturb the phono-input level control setting in any succeeding steps.

You are now set up to adjust both the input level controls for whatever other signal sources you have, and the output volume controls for those sources. If the sources are stereo, leave the function selector set on stereo; if they are monaural sources, switch to the monaural mode which feeds the input to both preamp outputs, or set the blend control for maximum blending.

Turn the volume controls on the signal sources about ⅔ of the way up. Then turn up the preamp input level controls for these signal sources to obtain approximately the same sound level, when you switch the input selector(s) to them, that you get from records at the same setting of the master volume control(s). For a stereo signal source such as a tape machine it will be necessary to make fine relative adjustments either of the source's output volume controls or of the preamp's input level controls for that source, so as to obtain proper balance between the speaker systems.

These input level control settings should be left as they are. The signal source output volume control settings should be marked clearly so that you can return to them easily for subsequent playing.

INDEX